CONTENTS

PREFACE

Essential Mathematics Book 8S has been written for pupils in Year 8 who are working within the National Curriculum Level 3–5 Tier.

There is no set path through the books but topics appear in the order suggested in the numerous strategy planning charts. Broadly speaking, the book is split into 6 parts with a Review Section for use as revision or test material at the end of each half-term.

The authors recognise that there is a wealth of ideas available for 'starter' activities and many developing opportunities to explore mathematics through the use of ICT. The purpose of this book is to provide the main material for pupils to work at in a systematic way which helps to build up their confidence.

No textbook will have the 'right' amount of material for every class and the authors believe that it is better to have too much material rather than too little.

Each topic is broken down into two sections. Section M is the main activity and should be suitable for all children at this level. Section E is the extension work. Pupils may move naturally onto this work after Section M, or teachers will judge that a number of students should *only* tackle Section E.

Explanations are kept to a minimum because it is assumed that teachers will explore each topic fully in line with the NNS guidance.

The authors are indebted to the contributions from David Rayner and Stephen Pearce.

Michael White

Peter Gibson

Year 7 material

Using and applying mathematics to solve problems

Applying mathematics and solving problems

89–90	• Investigate in a range of contexts:
192, 193	Shape, space and measures.
187, 188	• Break a complex calculation into simpler steps, choosing and using appropriate and efficient operations, methods.

Numbers and the number system

Place value, ordering and rounding

110–113	• Understand and use decimal notation and place value; multiply and divide integers and decimals by 10, 100, 1000, and explain the effect.
114, 115	• Round positive whole numbers to the nearest 10, 100 or 1000 and decimals to the nearest whole number.

Integers, powers and roots

5–7	• Understand negative numbers as positions on a number line; order, add and subtract positive and negative integers in context.
8, 9, 33	• Recognise and use multiples, factors (divisors), common factor, highest common factor and lowest common multiple in simple cases, and primes (less than 100).
11, 12	• Recognise the first few triangular numbers, squares of numbers to at least 12 × 12 and the corresponding roots.

Fractions, decimals, percentages, ratio and proportion

34, 35	• Simplify fractions by cancelling all common factors and identify equivalent fractions.
48	Convert terminating decimals to fractions, e.g. $0.23 = \frac{23}{100}$.
49, 50, 51, 52	• Begin to add and subtract simple fractions and those with common denominators; calculate simple fractions of quantities and measurements (whole-number answers); multiply a fraction by an integer.
53, 54	Calculate simple percentages.
194–199	• Understand the relationship between ratio and proportion; use direct proportion in simple contexts; use ratio notation, reduce a ratio to its simplest form and divide a quantity into two parts in a given ratio; solve simple problems about ratio and proportion using informal strategies.

Calculations

Number operations and the relationships between them

169	• Know and use the order of operations, including brackets.

Mental methods and rapid recall of number facts

58, 59	• Consolidate the rapid recall of number facts, including positive integer complements to 100 and multiplication facts to 10 × 10, and quickly derive associated division facts.

117, 164, 165	• Consolidate and **extend mental methods of calculation to include decimals, fractions and percentages,** accompanied where appropriate by suitable jottings; solve simple word problems mentally.

Written methods

120–122 173	• **Multiply and divide three-digit by two-digit whole numbers;** extend to multiplying and dividing decimals with one or two places by single-digit whole numbers.

Calculator methods

123, 124	• Carry out calculations with more than one step using brackets and the memory.
123, 124	• Enter numbers and interpret the display in different contexts (decimals, percentages, money, metric measures).

Algebra

Equations, formulae and identities

36, 37 137, 138	• Use letter symbols to represent unknown numbers or variables;.
139–142	• Construct and solve simple linear equations with integer coefficients (unknown on one side only) using an appropriate method (e.g. inverse operations).
39–41 143, 144	• Use simple formulae from mathematics and other subjects; substitute positive integers into simple linear expressions and formulae.

Sequences, functions and graphs

14, 15	• Generate and describe simple integer sequences.
16–18	• Generate sequences from practical contexts and describe the general term in simple cases.
98–101	• Generate coordinate pairs that satisfy a simple linear rule.
102–104	**Plot the graphs of simple linear functions,** where y is given explicitly in terms of x, on paper and using ICT.
178–183	Recognise straight-line graphs parallel to the x-axis or y-axis.
105–109 184–186	• Begin to plot and interpret the graphs of simple linear functions arising from real-life situations.

Shape, space and measures

Geometrical reasoning: lines, angles and shapes

19–21	• Use correctly the vocabulary, notation and labelling conventions for lines, angles and shapes.
22, 23	• **Know the sum of angles at a point, on a straight line and in a triangle,** and recognise vertically opposite angles.
200–202	• Use 2-D representations to visualise 3-D shapes and deduce some of their properties.

Transformations

130–136	• Recognise and visualise the transformation and symmetry of a 2-D shape:
	– reflection in given mirror lines, and line symmetry;
	– rotation about a given point, and rotation symmetry;
	– translation.

Algebra

Equations, formulae and identities

Sequences, functions and graphs

Shape, space and measures

Geometrical reasoning: lines, angles and shapes

Transformations

Coordinates

Construction

Measures and mensuration

Handling data

Specifying a problem, planning and collecting data

Processing and representing data, using ICT as appropriate

Interpreting and discussing results

Probability

Adding and Subtracting 1

On these pages you will practise adding and subtracting.

Ⓜ Part 1

(1)
```
  136
+  45
```

(7)
```
  257
   18
+ 175
```

(13)
```
  49.7
+  8.8
```

> *Remember.* To add or subtract decimals, line up the decimal points.

(2)
```
  145
+ 137
```

(8)
```
  374
   37
+ 104
```

(14)
```
  15.9
+  7.6
```

(3)
```
  157
+  55
```

(9)
```
  516
   47
+ 151
```

(15)
```
  40.2
+  9.8
```

(4)
```
  207
+  85
```

(10)
```
  315
  217
+  49
```

(16)
```
  16.95
+  4.37
```

(5)
```
  469
+  87
```

(11)
```
  259
  137
+ 407
```

(17)
```
  21.03
+  7.56
```

(6)
```
  103
   72
+ 264
```

(12)
```
  15.3
+  7.4
```

(18)
```
  141.7
+  18.3
```

Part 2

In Questions **(19)** to **(30)** write the numbers in columns and then subtract.

(19) 4183 – 726

(20) 4991 – 877

(21) 5168 – 1459

(22) 7791 – 576

(23) 18816 – 9457

(24) 2072 – 1345

(25) 751.2 – 180.5

(26) 573.89 – 82.51

(27) 541.7 – 326.05

(28) 485.2 – 19.85

(29) 96.58 – 40.85

(30) 30.63 – 21.46

E

Work out

① 17.65 + 13.41 + 6.77

② 51.42 + 8.71 + 10.02

③ 105.71 + 2.05 + 18.16

④ 71.9 + 18.03 + 0.75

⑤ 119.425 + 31.62 + 47.09

⑥ £14.75 + £8.02 + £25.79

⑦ £105.22 + £18.51 + £7.07

⑧ £1257.95 + £10.72 + £85.08

⑨ £59.65 + £27.61 + £38.19 + 72p

⑩ £62.40 + 85p + 91p + £3.87

Work out

⑪ 16.85 – 9.88

⑫ 7.08 – 3.54

⑬ 106.32 – 49.67

⑭ 259.11 – 174.59

⑮ 235.7 – 188.06

⑯ £29.42 – £12.88

⑰ £11.05 – £4.28

⑱ £76.15 – £29.37

⑲ £105.46 – £79.57

⑳ £203.50 – £127.66

㉑ Joe found a car costing just £25.
He needed to spend £116.50 to
fix it and £60 to tax it.
How much did it cost altogether?

㉒ A bracelet costs £17.80 and a nose stud costs £15.99.
(a) What is the total cost for both the bracelet and nose stud?
(b) How much change would you get from a £50 note?

㉓ On their wedding day, a husband and wife gave each other a gold ring. One ring
cost £85.90 and the other cost £50.85.
(a) What was the total cost?
(b) How much change would you get from £200?

㉔ A ski holiday costs £780 per adult and £530 per child. How much does it cost for
one adult and two children?

㉕ The times for the first three teams in a relay race were as follows: 1st 40.09, 2nd
41.33, 3rd 41.38.
(a) What was their total time?
(b) By how much did first beat second?

On this page you will practise long multiplication. (2 digit by 2 digit numbers)

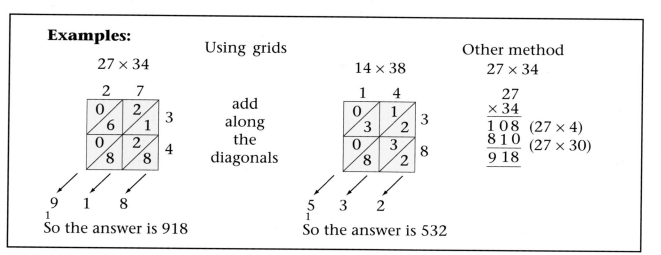

Examples:

Using grids   Other method

27×34

add along the diagonals

So the answer is 918

14×38

So the answer is 532

27×34

$$\begin{array}{r} 27 \\ \times\ 34 \\ \hline 1\ 08 \\ 8\ 1\ 0 \\ \hline 9\ 18 \end{array}$$

(27 × 4)
(27 × 30)

M

Work out.

1) 26×15

2) 23×16

3) 27×13

4) 14×32

5) 14×15

6) 31×22

7) 26×18

8) 17×25

9) Read the newspaper article below. Each leech requires 35 mg of blood. How much blood is needed for a dozen leeches?

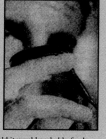

Blood lust satisfied

Hungry new arrivals at a zoo were saved when the staff became blood donors. A dozen leeches delivered to Drusillas in Alfriston, East Sussex, were craving fresh blood and the only way to satisfy them was to attach them to workers who volunteered to help. Gemma Walker, 25, an education worker at the zoo, said: "I was quite surprised at how quickly it attached itself. It drilled its head into my arm and as its teeth went in it felt a bit like being stung with nettles. I was told it would probably feed for about ten minutes but it kept going for well over an hour. It grew to about three times its size and then fell off." The leeches need feeding every two months or so, preferably on human blood.

E

Copy and complete.

1) $\begin{array}{r} 68 \\ \times\ 34 \end{array}$

2) $\begin{array}{r} 92 \\ \times\ 27 \end{array}$

3) $\begin{array}{r} 78 \\ \times\ 52 \end{array}$

4) $\begin{array}{r} 48 \\ \times\ 37 \end{array}$

5) $\begin{array}{r} 39 \\ \times\ 16 \end{array}$

6) $\begin{array}{r} 73 \\ \times\ 18 \end{array}$

7) $\begin{array}{r} 65 \\ \times\ 46 \end{array}$

8) $\begin{array}{r} 75 \\ \times\ 29 \end{array}$

9) $\begin{array}{r} 59 \\ \times\ 34 \end{array}$

10) $\begin{array}{r} 68 \\ \times\ 25 \end{array}$

11) Work out the total cost for 35 drinks at 32p each. Give your answer in pounds.

12) There are 34 rooms in a school and each room has 28 chairs. How many chairs are there altogether?

On this page you will practise long division.

Example

Work out $400 \div 16$

Step 1. Write out the 16 times table.   Step 2.

$1 \times 16 = 16$

$2 \times 16 = 32$

$3 \times 16 = 48$

$4 \times 16 = 64$

$5 \times 16 = 80$

$6 \times 16 = 96$

etc.

$$\begin{array}{r} 25 \\ 16\overline{)400} \\ -32\downarrow \\ \hline 80 \\ -80 \\ \hline \end{array}$$

- 16 into 40 goes 2 times
- $2 \times 16 = 32$
- $40 - 32 = 8$
- 'bring down' 0
- 16 into 80 goes 5 times
- $5 \times 16 = 80$
- $80 - 80 = 0$
- Answer is 25.

M

1 a) Write out the 14 times table up to 6×14

   [$1 \times 14 = 14$, $2 \times 14 = 28$ etc]

   b) Work out $14\overline{)476}$

2 a) Write out the 13 times table up to 6×13

   b) Work out $13\overline{)325}$

Work out

3 $13\overline{)546}$ **6** $14\overline{)336}$

4 $13\overline{)689}$ **7** $14\overline{)728}$

5 $13\overline{)533}$ **8** $14\overline{)350}$

9 A gardener charges £13 to mow a lawn. How many lawns can be mowed for £208?

E

1 Write out the times tables for 15, 18 and 26

Work out

2 $15\overline{)360}$ **6** $26\overline{)624}$

3 $18\overline{)630}$ **7** $15\overline{)795}$

4 $26\overline{)832}$ **8** $18\overline{)576}$

5 $18\overline{)738}$ **9** $26\overline{)858}$

10 It costs £23 per week to feed a leopard in a zoo. For how many weeks can it be fed for £621?

11 Eggs are packed twelve to a box. How many boxes are needed for 648 eggs?

12 A minibus can take 16 passengers. How many minibuses are needed for 368 passengers?

Negative Numbers

On these pages you will add and subtract negative numbers.

For adding and subtracting with negative numbers, a number line is very useful.

| + go up | | − go down |

−2
start here

+
go up

5
5 places

answer = 3

4
start here

−
go down

7
7 places

answer = −3

−1
start here

−
go down

2
2 places

answer = −3

Number line markings: 6, 5, 4, 3, 2, 1, 0, −1, −2, −3, −4, −5, −6

−10 −9 −8 −7 −6 −5 −4 −3 −2 −1 0 1 2 3 4 5 6 7 8 9 10 °C

D   B   A   C   E   F

1 What temperatures are shown by the letters above?

2 Give the rise in temperature between
- a) D and B
- b) B and E
- c) D and A
- d) B and C
- e) A and C
- f) D and C
- g) A and F
- h) B and F

3 What would the temperature be if it was:
- a) at B and rose 4°C?
- b) at A and fell 2°C?
- c) at F and fell 12°C?
- d) at C and rose 5°C?
- e) at E and fell 6°C?
- f) at D and rose 8°C?

4 Work out the following, using Question **3** answers to help:
- a) −6 + 4
- b) −3 −2
- c) −10 + 8
- d) +8 −12
- e) 5 − 6

(5) What would the temperature be if it was

- a) at E and fell 14°C?
- b) at A and fell 5°C?
- c) at B and rose 7°C?
- d) at B and fell 3°C?
- e) at E and fell 10°C?
- f) at C and fell 7°C?

(6) Work out the following, using Question **(5)** answers to help:

a) −6 − 3   b) 5 − 10   c) −6 + 7   d) 3 − 7   e) 5 − 14

Copy and complete the following tables.

(7)

Monday	Tuesday	Change
−3°C	2°C	+5°C
+2°C	−3°C	
8°C		−10°C
−5°C	0°C	
	−4°C	+4°C

(8)

Monday	Tuesday	Change
	7°C	−3°C
−5°C	−2°C	
7°C		−4°C
4°C	−2°C	
	−1°C	+1°C

In Questions **(9)** to **(20)** move up or down the thermometer to find the new temperature.

(9) The temperature is +8° and it falls by 3°.

(10) The temperature is +4° and it falls by 5°.

(11) The temperature is +2° and it falls by 6°.

(12) The temperature is −1° and it falls by 6°.

(13) The temperature is −5° and it rises by 1°.

(14) The temperature is −8° and it rises by 4°.

(15) The temperature is −3° and it rises by 7°.

(16) The temperature is +4° and it rises by 8°.

(17) The temperature is +9° and it falls by 14°.

(18) The temperature is −13° and it rises by 13°.

(19) The temperature is −6° and it falls by 5°.

(20) The temperature is −25° and it rises by 10°.

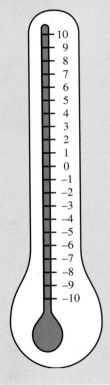

E

(1) Work out

a) −2 + 3	e) +4 − 7	i) −10 + 6	m) 6 − 4	q) −10 − 3
b) +3 − 7	f) +4 − 9	j) 0 − 6	n) 10 − 12	r) −5 − 5
c) −8 − 2	g) +2 − 11	k) −3 + 4	o) 6 − 7	s) −5 + 7 − 2
d) −7 + 5	h) −3 + 8	l) −5 + 8	p) −15 + 8	t) 8 − 3 + 2

2 Copy each sequence and fill in the missing numbers

a) –4 –2 0 ☐ 4 6 ☐

b) –6 –5 ☐ –3 ☐ –1 0

c) –7 ☐ ☐ –1 1 3 ☐

d) –9 –6 ☐ ☐ 3 ☐

e) –8 –3 ☐ ☐ 12 ☐

f) –11 ☐ ☐ –2 1

g) –12 ☐ ☐ ☐ 4

h) –15 –9 ☐ ☐ 9

i) ☐ ☐ –3 2 7

j) –9 –2 ☐ ☐ 19

Two signs together

The calculation 8 – (+ 3) can be read as '8 take away positive 3'.

Similarly 6 – (– 4) can be read as '6 take away negative 4'

It is possible to replace two signs next to each other by *one* sign as follows:

Remember: 'same signs: +'
'different signs: –'

$$+ \quad + \quad = \quad +$$
$$- \quad - \quad = \quad +$$
$$- \quad + \quad = \quad -$$
$$+ \quad - \quad = \quad -$$

When two adjacent signs have been replaced by one sign in this way, the calculation is completed using the number line as before.

Examples

a) $-7 + (-4)$
 $= -7 - 4$
 $= -11$

b) $8 + (-14)$
 $= 8 - 14$
 $= -6$

c) $5 - (+9)$
 $= 5 - 9$
 $= -4$

d) $6 - (-2)$
 $= 6 + 2$
 $= 8$

---

3 Work out

a) $5 + (-2)$

b) $4 + (-5)$

c) $6 + (-6)$

d) $4 + (-8)$

e) $8 - (+2)$

f) $7 - (+8)$

g) $3 - (-1)$

h) $4 - (-2)$

i) $6 - (-3)$

j) $4 - (-4)$

k) $9 - (+1)$

l) $10 - (+5)$

4 Work out

a) $4 - (-2)$

b) $6 - (-6)$

c) $8 + (-10)$

d) $3 + (-2)$

e) $8 + (+2)$

f) $7 - (+4)$

g) $6 - (-5)$

h) $4 - (-2)$

i) $10 + (-20)$

j) $15 + (-16)$

k) $9 + (-12)$

l) $-3 - (-4)$

On these pages you will find factors and multiples. You will also find highest common factors and lowest common multiples.

Remember:	A factor is a number which divides exactly into another number (there will be no remainder).
	Multiples are the numbers in a multiplication table.
	7, 14, 21, 28, 35,........ are multiples of 7.

Ⓜ

All the factors of 12 are | 1, 12 | | 2, 6 | | 3, 4 | ⟨ work out in pairs. ⟩

Write down all the factors of the following numbers:

(1) 9 (3 factors)   **(5)** 11 (2 factors)   **(9)** 42 (8 factors)

(2) 10 (4 factors)   **(6)** 22 (4 factors)   **(10)** 44 (6 factors)

(3) 17 (2 factors)   **(7)** 24 (8 factors)

(4) 8 (4 factors)   **(8)** 35 (4 factors)

What number belongs in the empty box below?

(11) 1, 3, 5 and 15 are all the factors of [   ]

(12) 1 and 7 are all the factors of [   ]

(13) 1, 2, 4, 5, 10 and 20 are all the factors of [   ]

(14) 16, 8, 4, 2 and 1 are all the factors of [   ]

Copy and complete the first 8 multiples of the number in the first box.

(15) | 6 | 12 | 18 | | | | | |

(16) | 25 | | | | | | | |

(17) | 8 | | | | | | | |

(18) | 12 | | | | | | | |

(19) | 20 | | | | | | | |

Write Yes or No.

(20) Is 63 a multiple of 9? ....   **(25)** Is 180 a multiple of 20? ....

(21) Is 511 a multiple of 5? ....   **(26)** Is 32 a multiple of 11? ....

(22) Is 60 a multiple of 15? ....   **(27)** Is 99 a multiple of 3? ....

(23) Is 56 a multiple of 7? ....   **(28)** Is 75 a multiple of 50? ....

(24) Is 82 a multiple of 4? ....   **(29)** Is 46 a multiple of 6? ....

Copy and draw a circle around the numbers which are *not* multiples of:

(30) [2] 27 18 45 30 78   **(32)** [3] 15 23 27 60 31

(31) [6] 18 26 24 63 30   **(33)** [5] 24 35 70 52 105

Highest Common Factor.

Example

The factors of 12 are 1, 2, 3, (4), 6, 12   The *highest* factor in both lists is 4.

The factors of 16 are 1, 2, (4), 8,16   This is called the
Highest Common Factor (HCF)

Lowest Common Multiple.

Example

The multiples of 2 are 2, 4, 6, 8, (10), 12, ...   The *lowest* number in both lists is 10.

The multiples of 5 are 5, (10), 15, 20, ...   This is called the
Lowest Common Multiple (LCM).

The Lowest Common Multiple of two or more numbers is the smallest number which each of these numbers will divide into.

E

The factors of 12:   1, 2, 3, (4), 6, 12   The highest factor shared

The factors of 16:   1, 2, (4), 8, 16   by both 12 and 16 is 4.

Find the highest factor shared by these pairs of numbers.

(1) 8 and 12   **(3)** 20 and 30   **(5)** 12 and 18   **(7)** 21 and 35   **(9)** 36 and 54

(2) 12 and 15   **(4)** 15 and 25   **(6)** 24 and 40   **(8)** 18 and 24   **(10)** 36 and 48

Find the lowest common multiple of each of these pairs or groups of numbers.

(11) 2 and 3   **(13)** 4 and 10   **(15)** 5 and 9

(12) 3 and 4   **(14)** 2 and 7   **(16)** 10 and 8

(17)

Number	Factors
8	1, 2, 4, 8
10	1, 2, 5, 10

What is the Highest Common Factor of 8 and 10?

(18)

Number	Factors
6	1, 2, 3, 6
15	1, 3, 5, 15

What is the Highest Common Factor of 6 and 15?

Find the Highest Common Factors of the following pairs of numbers:

(19) 10 and 30   **(21)** 12 and 30   **(23)** 18 and 27

(20) 25 and 30   **(22)** 21 and 28   **(24)** 56 and 24

On these pages you will learn to recognise square numbers, triangular numbers and how to find square roots.

Remember:

When a number is multiplied by itself you get a square number.

They are called square numbers because they make square patterns.

$1^2 = 1 \times 1 = 1$ $2^2 = 2 \times 2 = 4$ $3^2 = 3 \times 3 = 9$ $4^2 = 4 \times 4 = 16$

When numbers make triangular patterns like below, they are called triangular numbers.

1   3   6   10

The square root of 16 is 4 because 4 multiplied by itself is 16.

$4 \times 4 = 16$ so we say $\sqrt{16} = 4$ ($\sqrt{16}$ means the square root of 16)

$\sqrt{36} = 6$ because $6 \times 6 = 36$ ($6 \times itself$ makes 36)

Ⓜ

① Complete this table up to 12^2.

$1^2 = 1 \times 1 = 1$

$2^2 = 2 \times 2 = 4$

$3^2 = 3 \times 3 = 9$

Work out

② $4^2 + 2^2$

③ $5^2 + 3^2$

④ $6^2 + 1^2$

⑤ $5^2 - 3^2$

⑥ $8^2 - 6^2$

⑦ $6^2 - 3^2$

⑧ $10^2 + 7^2$

⑨ $9^2 + 1^2$

⑩ $8^2 + 5^2$

⑪ $9^2 - 4^2$

⑫ $10^2 - 6^2$

⑬ $8^2 - 7^2$

⑭ Which of these numbers is a triangular number?

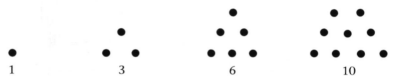

32   11   6   28   20   14   15   7   13

⑮ Write down the square root of 25.

⑯ Write down the square root of 9.

Work out

⑰ $\sqrt{49}$

⑱ $\sqrt{4}$

⑲ $\sqrt{64}$

⑳ $\sqrt{100}$

㉑ $\sqrt{16} + \sqrt{25}$

㉒ $\sqrt{81} - \sqrt{25}$

㉓ $\sqrt{64} - \sqrt{36}$

㉔ $\sqrt{100} + \sqrt{1}$

E

Happy Numbers

- a) Take any number, say 23.
  b) Square the digits and add: $2^2 + 3^2 = 4 + 9 = 13$
  c) Repeat b) for the answer: $1^2 + 3^2 = 1 + 9 = 10$
  d) Repeat b) for the answer: $1^2 + 0^2 = 1$

  23 is a so-called 'happy' number because it ends in one.

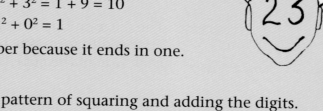

- Take another number, say 7.

  Write 7 as 07 to maintain the pattern of squaring and adding the digits. Here is the sequence:

  $$07$$
  $$0 + 49 = 49$$
  $$16 + 81 = 97$$

  So 7 is a happy number also.

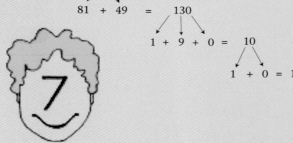

  $$81 + 49 = 130$$
  $$1 + 9 + 0 = 10$$
  $$1 + 0 = 1$$

With practice you may be able to do the arithmetic in your head and write:
$07 \rightarrow 49 \rightarrow 97 \rightarrow 130 \rightarrow 10 \rightarrow 1$.

You may find it helpful to make a list of the square numbers $1^2, 2^2, 3^2, ... 9^2$.

- Your task is to find all the happy numbers from 1 to 100 and to circle them on a grid like the one shown.

  Remember: Good mathematicians always look for short cuts and for ways of reducing the working.

  So think about what you are doing and good luck!
  As a final check you should find that there are 20 happy numbers from 1 to 100.

1	2	3	4	5	6	7	8	9	10
11	12	13	14	15	16	17	18	19	20
21	22	23	24	25	26	27	28	29	30
31	32	33	34	35	36	37	38	39	40
41	42	43	44	45	46	47	48	49	50
51	52	53	54	55	56	57	58	59	60
61	62	63	64	65	66	67	68	69	70
71	72	73	74	75	76	77	78	79	80
81	82	83	84	85	86	87	88	89	90
91	92	93	94	95	96	97	98	99	100

On these pages you will learn to use powers.

Cube numbers

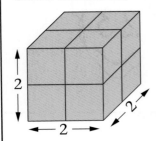

← The diagram opposite shows 8 unit cubes arranged to form one larger cube.
Each side of the cube is 2 units long.

- We say '2 cubed = 8'
  We write this as $2^3 = 8$
  We work it out like this: 2^3

$$= 2 \times 2 \times 2$$
$$= 4 \times 2$$
$$= 8$$

the small 3 means 'multiply 3 lots of 2 together,'
Not $3 \times 2 = 6$

M

4^3 means $4 \times 4 \times 4$.

Copy and complete the following:

(1) 3^3 means .... (4) 8^3 means ....

(2) 5^3 means .... (5) 10^3 means ....

(3) 6^3 means .... (6) 7^3 means ....

$2 \times 2 \times 2$ is the same as 2^3.

Write the following in the shorter way.

(7) $9 \times 9 \times 9$ is the same as.......... (9) $10 \times 10 \times 10$ is the same as..........

(8) $6 \times 6 \times 6$ is the same as.......... (10) $12 \times 12 \times 12$ is the same as..........

Remember we say that *15 cubed* is written as 15^3 which means $15 \times 15 \times 15$.

(11) Copy and complete this table. You may need a *calculator* to help you.

We say	We write	We work out	Answer
4 cubed	4^3	$4 \times 4 \times 4$	
3 cubed		$3 \times 3 \times 3$	
6 cubed	6^3		216
5 cubed			
		$9 \times 9 \times 9$	
	10^3		

$2 \times 2 \times 2$ is written as 2^3

$2 \times 2 \times 2 \times 2$ is written as 2^4

The small 4 means multiply 4 lots of 2 together

For 2^4 we say '2 *to the power 4*'

For 2^5 we say '2 *to the power 5*'

E

3^5 means $3 \times 3 \times 3 \times 3 \times 3$

Copy and complete the following:

1) 10^3 means ....

2) 7^5 means ....

3) 8^4 means ....

4) 3^4 means ....

5) 2^7 means ....

6) 12^3 means ....

7) 5^5 means ....

8) 8^6 means ....

$7 \times 7 \times 7 \times 7$ means '7 to the power 4' which is written as 7^4.

Write the following in this shorter way:

9) $5 \times 5 \times 5 \times 5$ means '5 to the power 4' which is written as.........

10) $6 \times 6 \times 6 \times 6 \times 6$ means '6 to the power 5' which is written as.........

11) $2 \times 2 \times 2 \times 2 \times 2 \times 2$ means '2 to the power 6' which is written as.........

12) Copy and complete this table, *using a calculator* to help you obtain the answers.

We say	We write	We work out	Answer
2 to the power 4	2^4	$2 \times 2 \times 2 \times 2$	16
3 to the power 4		$3 \times 3 \times 3 \times 3$	
4 to the power 4	4^4		256
5 to the power 2			
	6^5		7776
8 to the power 5		$8 \times 8 \times 8 \times 8 \times 8$	
		$9 \times 9 \times 9$	
	3^9		
10 to the power 2			
2 to the power 10			

On these pages you will look at number patterns and the rules to make patterns.

Ⓜ

Write the first 4 numbers of these sequences:

	Start at	Rule
①	3	Add 4
②	6	Add 3
③	10	Subtract 2
④	35	Subtract 5
⑤	8	Add 3
⑥	5	Add 5
⑦	9	Add 9
⑧	50	Subtract 5
⑨	64	Subtract 8
⑩	65	Subtract 10

	Start at	Rule
⑪	2	× 4
⑫	32	÷ 2
⑬	128	÷ 4
⑭	1	× 4
⑮	0	× 3
⑯	625	÷ 5
⑰	81	÷ 3
⑱	6	× 2
⑲	5	× 3
⑳	3	× 10

Write down the missing numbers for each question:

㉑ 10, 14, ☐, 22, ☐

㉒ 18, 15, ☐, 9, ☐

㉓ 4, 8, 16, ☐, ☐

㉔ –10, ☐, –6, ☐, –2

㉕ 81, 27, 9, ☐, ☐

㉖ 12, 14, ☐, 18, ☐

㉗ 40, 20, 10, ☐, ☐

㉘ 21, 17, 13, ☐, ☐

㉙ –10, ☐, –30, ☐, –50

㉚ 71, 67, 63, ☐, ☐

In Questions ㉛ to ㊱, find the rule in the empty box.

㉛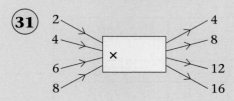

㉜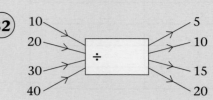

㉝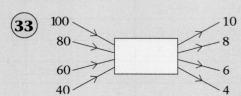

㉞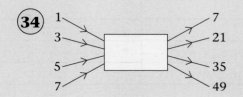

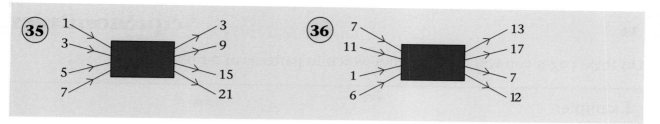

(35) 1, 3, 5, 7 → 3, 9, 15, 21

(36) 7, 11, 1, 6 → 13, 17, 7, 12

E

For each question below, copy and complete the table of numbers. Use the diagrams to help.

The first question has been done for you.

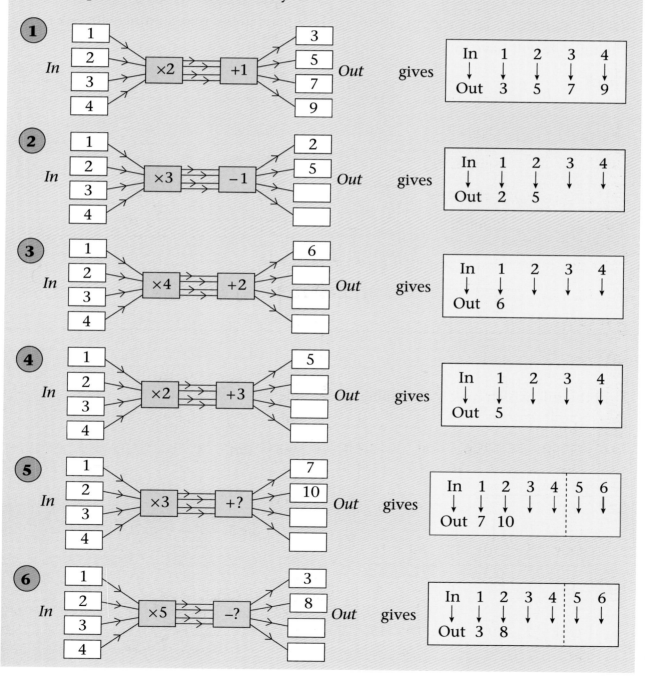

1 In: 1, 2, 3, 4 → ×2 → +1 → Out: 3, 5, 7, 9 gives

In	1	2	3	4
↓	↓	↓	↓	↓
Out	3	5	7	9

2 In: 1, 2, 3, 4 → ×3 → −1 → Out: 2, 5 gives

In	1	2	3	4
↓	↓	↓	↓	↓
Out	2	5		

3 In: 1, 2, 3, 4 → ×4 → +2 → Out: 6 gives

In	1	2	3	4
↓	↓	↓	↓	↓
Out	6			

4 In: 1, 2, 3, 4 → ×2 → +3 → Out: 5 gives

In	1	2	3	4
↓	↓	↓	↓	↓
Out	5			

5 In: 1, 2, 3, 4 → ×3 → +? → Out: 7, 10 gives

In	1	2	3	4	5	6
↓	↓	↓	↓	↓	↓	↓
Out	7	10				

6 In: 1, 2, 3, 4 → ×5 → −? → Out: 3, 8 gives

In	1	2	3	4	5	6
↓	↓	↓	↓	↓	↓	↓
Out	3	8				

On these pages you will find the rules which fit patterns of numbers.

Example:

Find the rule which makes this table.

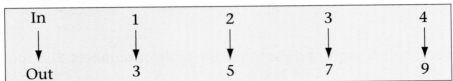

In	1	2	3	4
Out	3	5	7	9

The difference between the 'Out' numbers is 2.

If all the differences are the same, there will be 2 parts to the rule, starting with $\boxed{\times 2}$

The full rule will have to be $\boxed{\times 2}$ $\boxed{+1}$.

Check

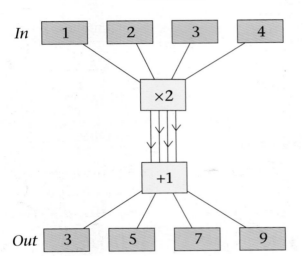

In | 1 | 2 | 3 | 4

$\times 2$

$+1$

Out | 3 | 5 | 7 | 9   The rule works!

M

Find the rule which makes each table. Each table will have 2 parts.

(1)
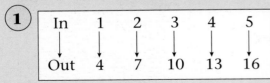

In	1	2	3	4	5
Out	4	7	10	13	16

Rule?

$\boxed{\times 3}$ and $\boxed{?}$

(2)

In	1	2	3	4	5
Out	8	10	12	14	16

Rule?

$\boxed{\times 2}$ and $\boxed{?}$

(3)
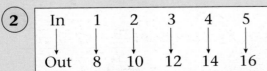
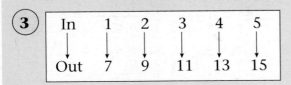

In	1	2	3	4	5
Out	7	9	11	13	15

Rule?

$\boxed{\times ?}$ and $\boxed{+5}$

4

In	1	2	3	4	5
Out	1	6	11	16	21

Rule?

☐ and ☐ −4

5

In	1	2	3	4	5
Out	3	7	11	15	19

Rule?

☐ and ☐

6

In	1	2	3	4	5
Out	5	8	11	14	17

Rule?

☐ and ☐

7

In	1	2	3	4	5
Out	6	11	16	21	26

Rule?

☐ and ☐

8 Shapes are made from matchsticks as follows:

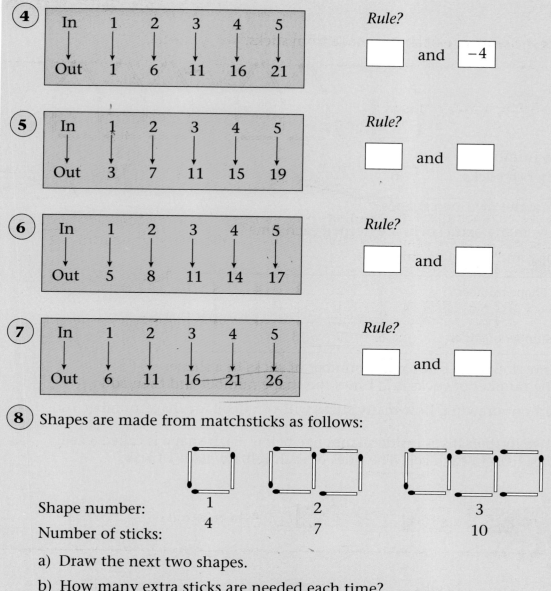

Shape number:	1	2	3
Number of sticks:	4	7	10

a) Draw the next two shapes.

b) How many extra sticks are needed each time?

c) Copy and complete this table:

Shape number	1	2	3	4	5
Number of sticks	4	7	10		

d) Look at the difference between each 'number of sticks' number in the table. Use this to copy and complete the following:

The number of sticks is … times the shape number and then add …

1 Here is the sequence of shapes made from sticks.

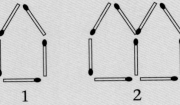

Shape number: 1   2   3
Number of sticks: 5   9   13

a) Draw the next two shapes.

b) How many extra sticks are needed each time?

c) Copy and complete this table:

Shape number	1	2	3	4	5
Number of sticks	5	9	13		

d) Write down the rule for the number of sticks in a shape:
   'The number of sticks is ... times the shape number and then add ...'

e) Without drawing, how many sticks will you need for shape number 100?

2 Bees live in their hives inside shapes like below. Each shape is called a cell.
One bee lives in each cell. The sides of each cell are made of wax.

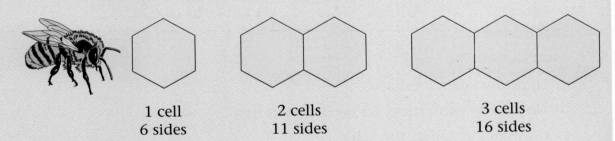

1 cell   2 cells   3 cells
6 sides   11 sides   16 sides

a) How many sides are needed for 4 cells?

b) How many sides are needed for 5 cells?

c) Copy and complete this table:

Number of cells	1	2	3	4	5
Number of sides	6	11	16		

d) Find the rule which works out how many sides there are if you know the
   number of cells:

   'The number of sides is ... times the number of cells and then add ...'

On these pages you will learn how to name lines, angles and shapes.

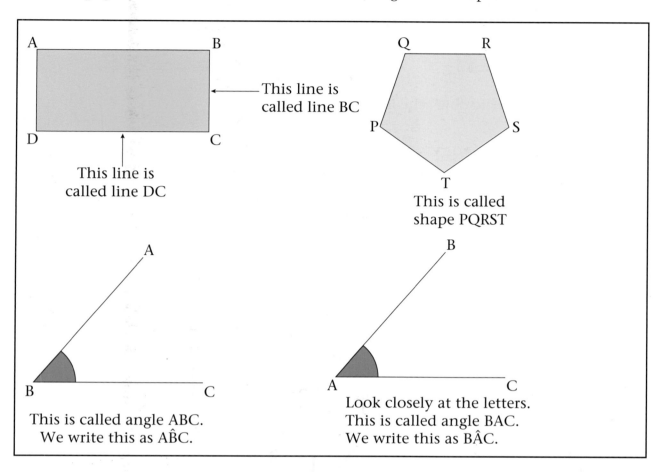

This line is called line BC

This line is called line DC

This is called shape PQRST

This is called angle ABC.
We write this as AB̂C.

Look closely at the letters.
This is called angle BAC.
We write this as BÂC.

M

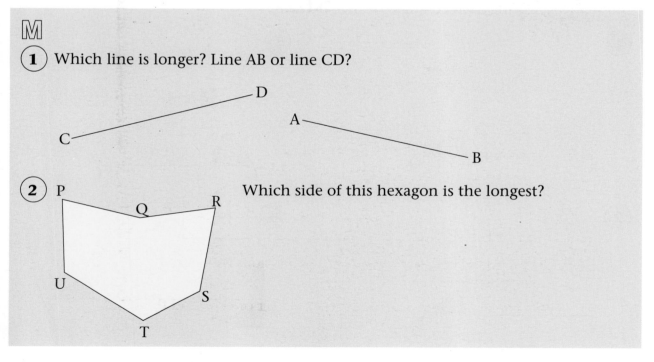

1 Which line is longer? Line AB or line CD?

2 Which side of this hexagon is the longest?

3 Write down the name of the largest rectangle below:

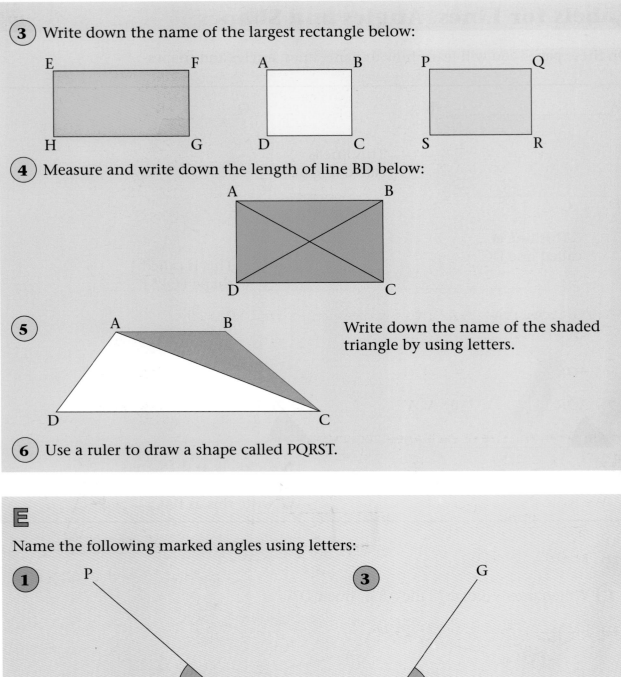

4 Measure and write down the length of line BD below:

5 Write down the name of the shaded triangle by using letters.

6 Use a ruler to draw a shape called PQRST.

E

Name the following marked angles using letters:

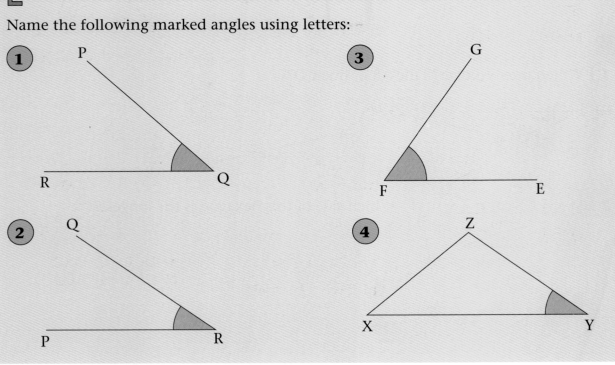

1

2

3

4

21

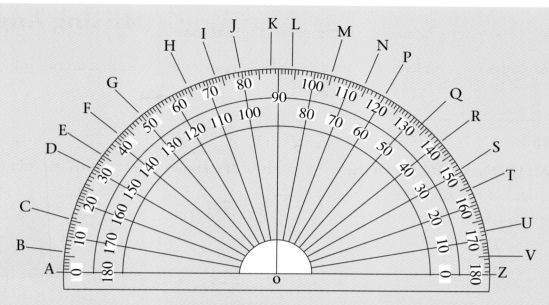

Use the above protractor. Give the measurement of each angle.

5 AÔE　　**8** AÔC　　**11** ZÔM　　**14** ZÔC

6 AÔJ　　**9** AÔH　　**12** ZÔJ　　**15** ZÔP

7 AÔR　　**10** AÔV　　**13** ZÔR　　**16** ZÔE

Write down the size of each angle requested.

17

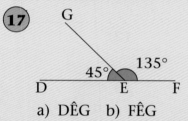

a) DÊG　b) FÊG

18

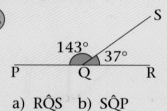

a) RQ̂S　b) SQ̂P

19

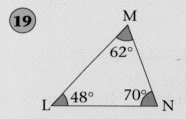

a) MN̂L　b) NL̂M　c) LM̂N

20

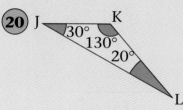

a) KĴL　b) JL̂K
c) JK̂L

21

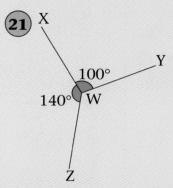

a) ZŴX　b) XŴY

22

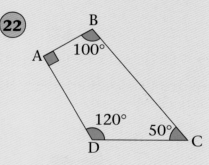

a) DĈB　b) DÂB
c) CD̂A　d) AB̂C

On these pages you will learn to calculate angles on a straight line, at a point, in a triangle and to recognise vertically opposite angles.

Examples

- ANGLES ON A STRAIGHT LINE

  The sum of the angles on a straight line is 180°.

  $x + 57° = 180°$

  $x = 123°$

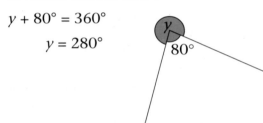

- ANGLES AT A POINT

  A whole turn is 360°.

  $y + 80° = 360°$

  $y = 280°$

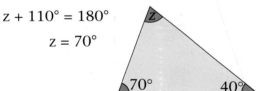

- ANGLES IN A TRIANGLE

  The sum of the angles in a triangle is 180°.

  $z + 110° = 180°$

  $z = 70°$

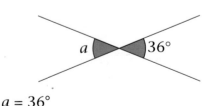

- VERTICALLY OPPOSITE ANGLES

  When two lines intersect the opposite angles are equal.

  $a = 36°$

  The angles 36° and a are vertically opposite.

Ⓜ

Find the angles marked with the letters.

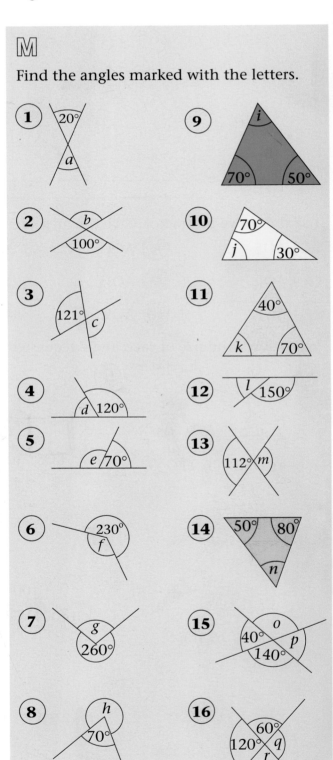

1. 20° / a

2. b / 100°

3. 121° / c

4. d 120°

5. e 70°

6. 230° / f

7. g / 260°

8. h / 70°

9. i / 70° 50°

10. 70° / j 30°

11. 40° / k 70°

12. l 150°

13. 112° m

14. 50° 80° / n

15. 40° o / 140° p

16. 60° / 120° q / r

E

Find the angles marked with the letters.

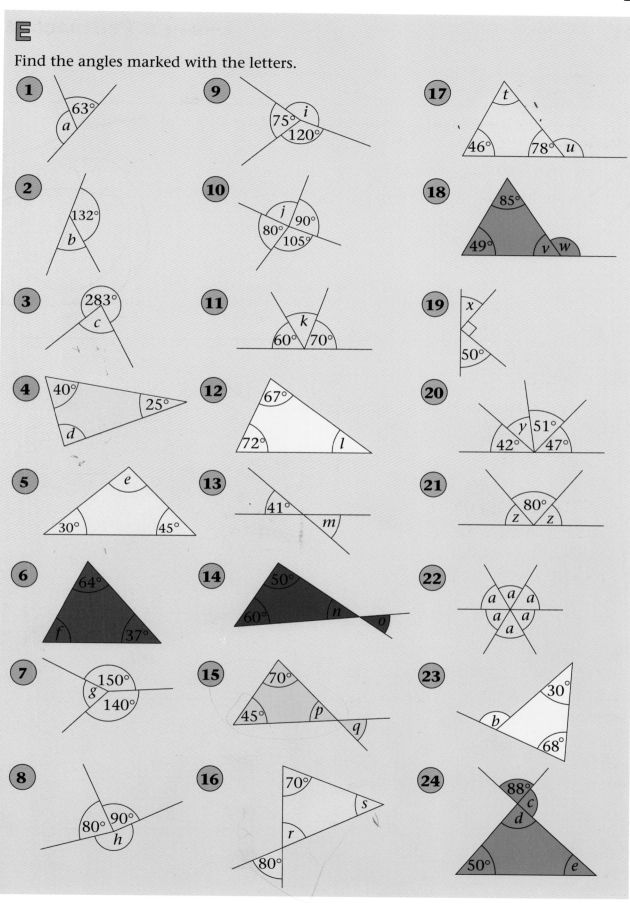

On these pages you will measure and draw angles accurately.

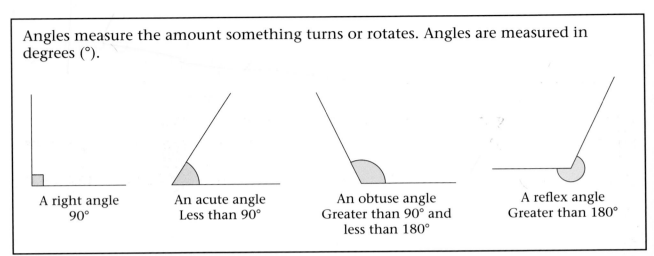

Angles measure the amount something turns or rotates. Angles are measured in degrees (°).

A right angle
90°

An acute angle
Less than 90°

An obtuse angle
Greater than 90° and
less than 180°

A reflex angle
Greater than 180°

Ⓜ

Using a protractor, measure the following angles.

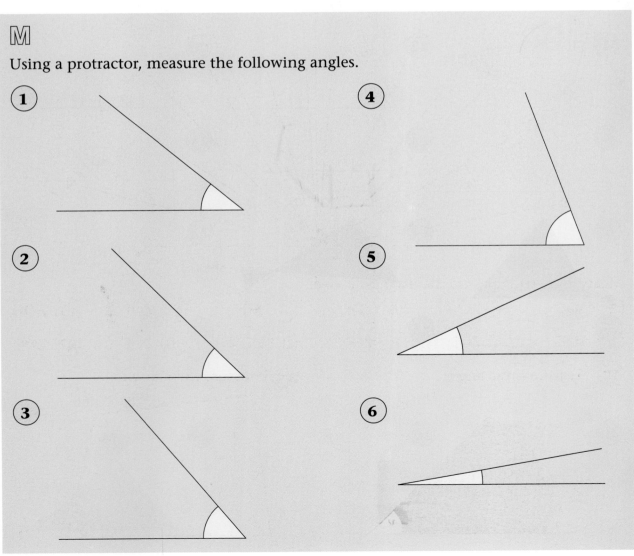

① ② ③ ④ ⑤ ⑥

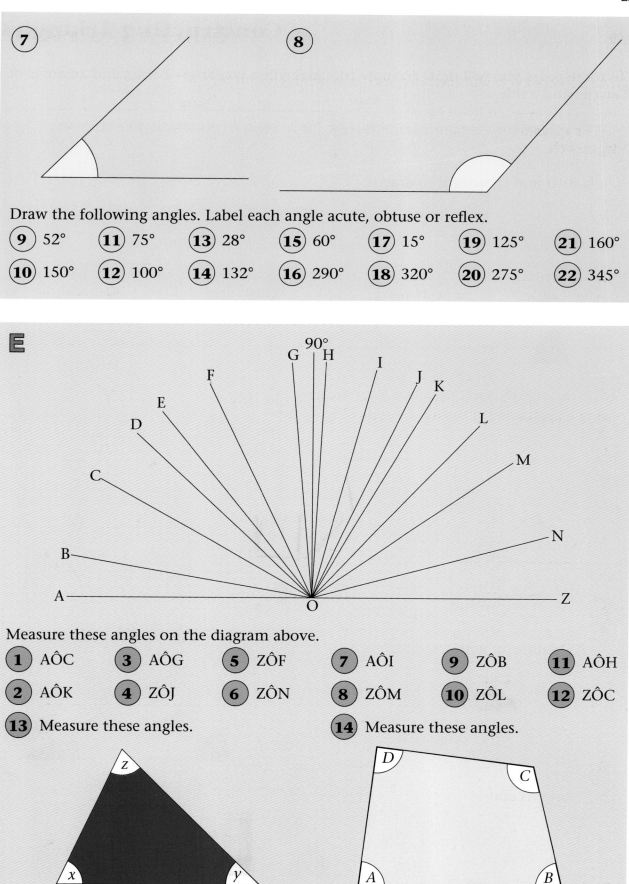

(7)

(8)

Draw the following angles. Label each angle acute, obtuse or reflex.

(9) 52°   **(11)** 75°   **(13)** 28°   **(15)** 60°   **(17)** 15°   **(19)** 125°   **(21)** 160°

(10) 150°   **(12)** 100°   **(14)** 132°   **(16)** 290°   **(18)** 320°   **(20)** 275°   **(22)** 345°

E

Measure these angles on the diagram above.

(1) AÔC   **(3)** AÔG   **(5)** ZÔF   **(7)** AÔI   **(9)** ZÔB   **(11)** AÔH

(2) AÔK   **(4)** ZÔJ   **(6)** ZÔN   **(8)** ZÔM   **(10)** ZÔL   **(12)** ZÔC

(13) Measure these angles.   **(14)** Measure these angles.

On these pages you will draw accurate triangles when you know 2 sides and an angle or 2 angles and a side.

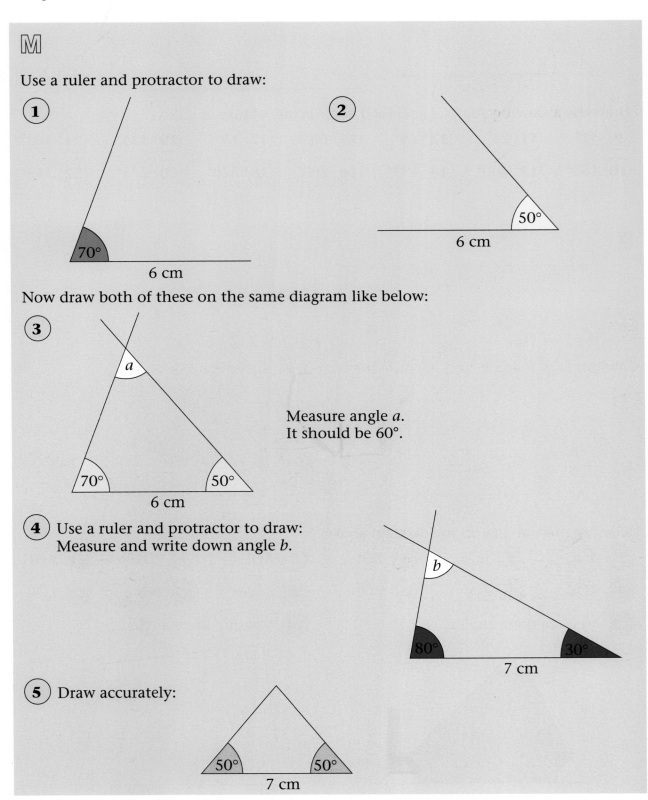

Ⓜ

Use a ruler and protractor to draw:

1 70° 6 cm

2 50° 6 cm

Now draw both of these on the same diagram like below:

3 a 70° 50° 6 cm

Measure angle a.
It should be 60°.

4 Use a ruler and protractor to draw:
Measure and write down angle b.

b 80° 30° 7 cm

5 Draw accurately:

50° 50° 7 cm

Use a ruler and protractor to draw:

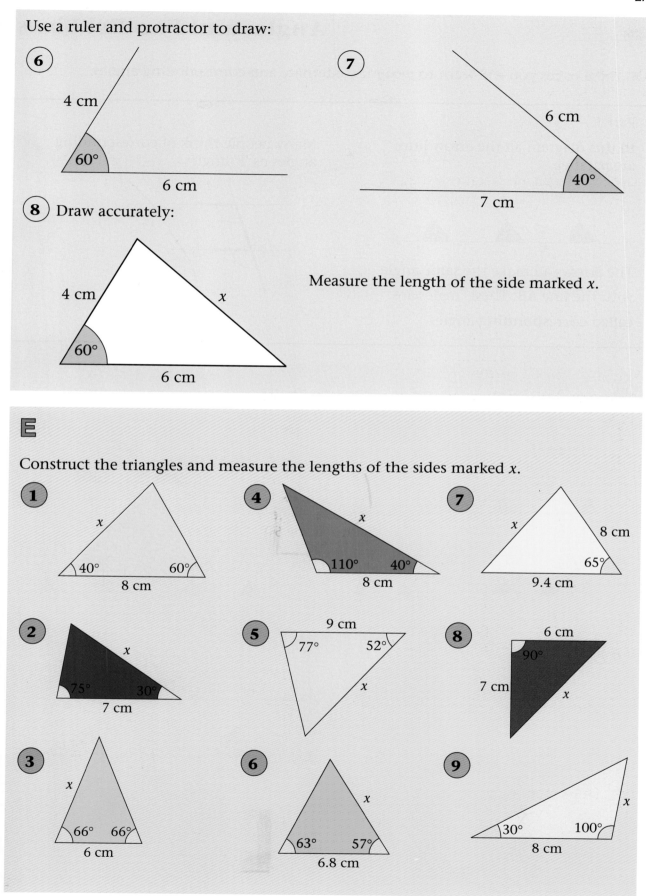

6

4 cm

60°

6 cm

7

6 cm

40°

7 cm

8 Draw accurately:

4 cm

x

60°

6 cm

Measure the length of the side marked *x*.

E

Construct the triangles and measure the lengths of the sides marked *x*.

1

x

40°   60°

8 cm

4

x

110°   40°

8 cm

7

x   8 cm

65°

9.4 cm

2

x

75°   30°

7 cm

5

9 cm

77°   52°

x

8

6 cm

90°

7 cm

x

3

x

66°   66°

6 cm

6

x

63°   57°

6.8 cm

9

x

30°   100°

8 cm

On these pages you will learn to recognise alternate and corresponding angles.

Part 1

In this diagram all the arrow lines are parallel.

The arrows all make the same angle with the line AB. These angles are called **corresponding** angles.

Many people think of corresponding angles as 'F' angles.

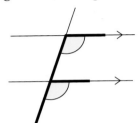

M

Find the size of the following angles, marked with letters

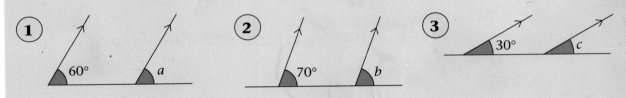

(1) 60°   a

(2) 70°   b

(3) 30°   c

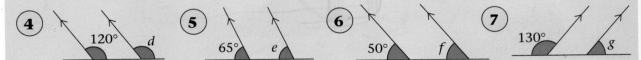

(4) 120°   d

(5) 65°   e

(6) 50°   f

(7) 130°   g

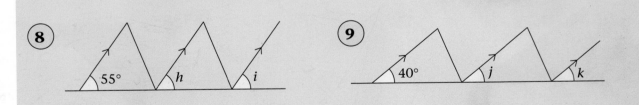

(8) 55°   h   i

(9) 40°   j   k

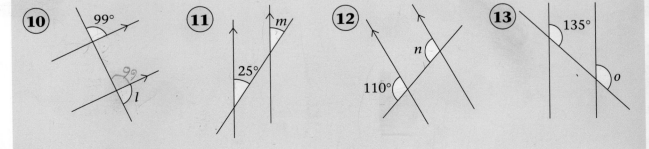

(10) 99°   l

(11) 25°   m

(12) 110°   n

(13) 135°   o

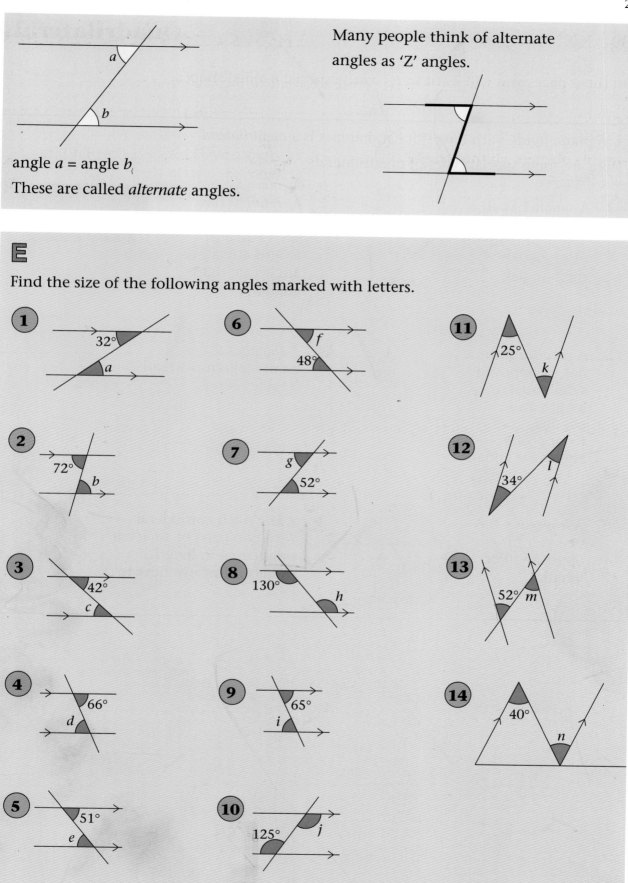

angle *a* = angle *b*

These are called *alternate* angles.

Many people think of alternate angles as 'Z' angles.

E

Find the size of the following angles marked with letters.

1 32° *a*

6 *f* 48°

11 25° *k*

2 72° *b*

7 *g* 52°

12 34° *l*

3 42° *c*

8 130° *h*

13 52° *m*

4 66° *d*

9 65° *i*

14 40° *n*

5 51° *e*

10 125° *j*

On these pages you will learn to recognise special 4-sided shapes.

- A plane figure with four sides and angles is a *quadrilateral*

Here are some special types of quadrilaterals:

1 A *square* has all its sides equal in length and all its angles are right angles.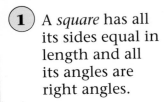

2 A *rectangle* has pairs of opposite sides equal in length and all its angles are right angles.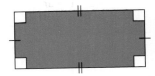

3 A *parallelogram* has its opposite sides equal in length and parallel. Its opposite angles are equal.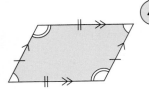

4 A *rhombus* is a parallelogram with all its sides equal.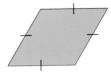

5 A *trapezium* has one pair of opposite sides parallel.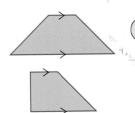

6 A *kite* is a quadrilateral with two pairs of adjacent sides equal in length. (Adjacent means 'next to'.)

M

1 Write down the letter for which bucket each of the 6 quadrilaterals will drop into when they pass through the sorting machine.

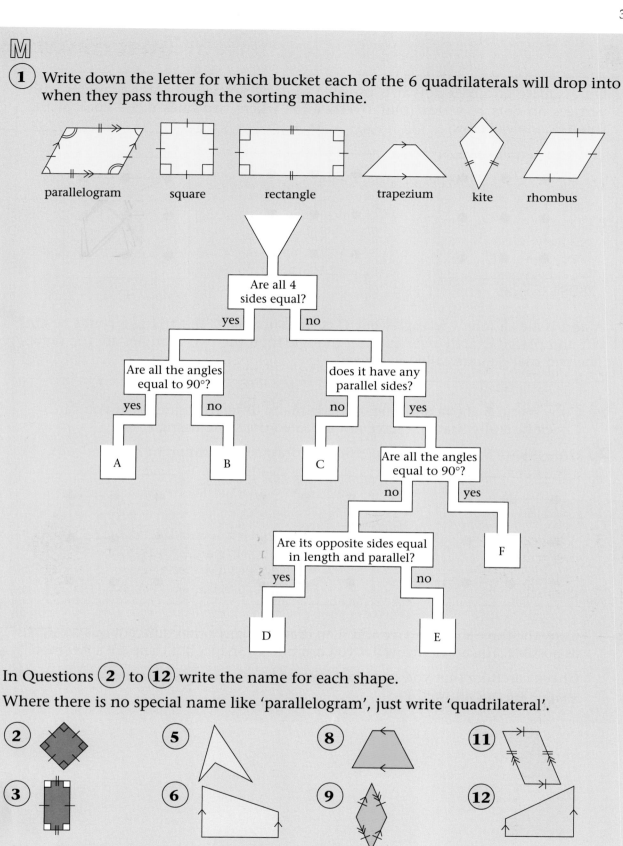

parallelogram   square   rectangle   trapezium   kite   rhombus

In Questions **2** to **12** write the name for each shape.

Where there is no special name like 'parallelogram', just write 'quadrilateral'.

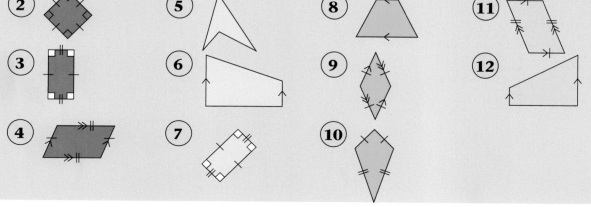

On a square grid of 9 dots it is possible to draw several different triangles with vertices on dots. A vertex (plural vertices) is where two lines meet. Look at the three examples below:

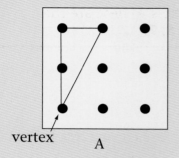

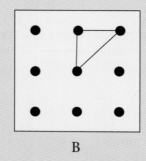

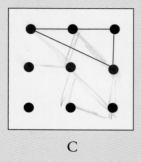

vertex   A   B   C

A and B are different triangles but C is the same as A. If a triangle could be cut out and placed exactly over another triangle then the two triangles are the same. The two triangles are called *congruent*.

1   Copy A and B above and then draw as many different triangles as you can. Check carefully that you have not repeated the same triangle.

2   On a grid of 9 dots it is also possible to draw several different *quadrilaterals*.

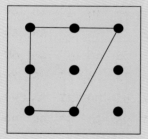

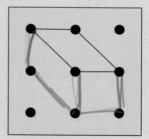

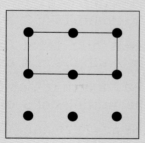

Copy the three shapes above and then draw as many other different quadrilaterals as possible. You are doing well if you can find 12 shapes but there are a few more!

Check carefully that you have not repeated the same quadrilateral. (Congruent shapes are not allowed.)

On these pages you will find prime numbers.

> *Remember.*
>
> A prime number can only be divided by two different numbers. (These are the number 1 and itself). The first four prime numbers are 2, 3, 5, 7, ...

THE SIEVE OF ERASTOSTHENES

Erastosthenes was a famous mathematician in Ancient Greece. He discovered a way of finding prime numbers known as the 'Sieve of Erastosthenes'.

Use five different coloured pens or pencils.
Copy the grid below.

Follow the directions to find the prime numbers to 100.

(1) Cross out 1 with a pencil.

(2) Draw a circle around 2, 3, 5 and 7 with the same pencil.

(3) Use a different colour. Cross out all the multiples of 2, leaving 2 itself.

(4) Use a third colour. Cross out all the multiples of 3, except for 3.

(5) Use a fourth colour. Cross out all the multiples of 5, except for 5.

(6) Use a fifth colour. Cross out all the multiples of 7, except for 7.

(7) Use your first colour again. Draw circles around all the numbers that are left.

These are the prime numbers to 100.

(8)

1	2	3	4	5	6	7	8	9	10
11	12	13	14	15	16	17	18	19	20
21	22	23	24	25	26	27	28	29	30
31	32	33	34	35	36	37	38	39	40
41	42	43	44	45	46	47	48	49	50
51	52	53	54	55	56	57	58	59	60
61	62	63	64	65	66	67	68	69	70
71	72	73	74	75	76	77	78	79	80
81	82	83	84	85	86	87	88	89	90
91	92	93	94	95	96	97	98	99	100

How many prime numbers have you found?

Write out the prime numbers.

Write down the numbers in each group which are not prime numbers.

(1) 5 6 7 8

(2) 7 10 13 16

(3) 12 17 23 21

(4) 28 29 31 33 35

Write down the next prime number after:

(5) 25

(6) 38

(7) 65

(8) 80

On this page you will learn to recognise equivalent fractions.

Equivalent fractions are fractions that look different but are the same.

Examples

 $\dfrac{2}{5} = \dfrac{4}{10}$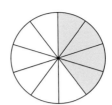

$\dfrac{3}{4} = \dfrac{6}{8}$

Ⓜ Part 1

Write the equivalent fractions shown by the shaded areas in each pair of diagrams.

①

⑤

⑨

②

⑥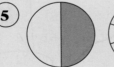

⑩

③

⑦

⑪

④

⑧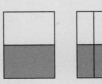

⑫

Part 2

whole		1
half		$\frac{1}{2}$
quarter		$\frac{1}{4}$
eighth		$\frac{1}{8}$

whole		1
half		$\frac{1}{2}$
third		$\frac{1}{3}$
sixth		$\frac{1}{6}$

whole		1
half		$\frac{1}{2}$
fifth		$\frac{1}{5}$
tenth		$\frac{1}{10}$

Use the fraction charts. Copy and complete these equivalent fractions by filling in the box.

1. $\frac{1}{2} = \frac{7}{8}$
2. $\frac{1}{3} = \frac{2}{6}$
3. $\frac{3}{5} = \frac{\square}{10}$
4. $\frac{1}{4} = \frac{\square}{16}$
5. $\frac{1}{6} = \frac{\square}{12}$
6. $\frac{1}{10} = \frac{\square}{20}$
7. $\frac{5}{8} = \frac{\square}{16}$
8. $\frac{1}{2} = \frac{\square}{12}$
9. $\frac{7}{10} = \frac{\square}{20}$
10. $\frac{3}{4} = \frac{\square}{8}$
11. $\frac{2}{3} = \frac{\square}{12}$
12. $\frac{4}{5} = \frac{\square}{20}$
13. $\frac{1}{2} = \frac{\square}{16}$
14. $\frac{5}{6} = \frac{\square}{12}$
15. $\frac{3}{10} = \frac{\square}{20}$

E

You can change a fraction to an equivalent fraction.

BY CANCELLING

Example

$\frac{8 \ (\div 4)}{12 \ (\div 4)} = \frac{2}{3}$

BY MULTIPLYING

Example

$\frac{2 \ (\times 3)}{5 \ (\times 3)} = \frac{6}{15}$

Copy and complete these equivalent fractions by filling in the box.

1. $\frac{2}{3} = \frac{\square}{9}$
2. $\frac{1}{4} = \frac{\square}{20}$
3. $\frac{1}{2} = \frac{\square}{14}$
4. $\frac{1}{3} = \frac{\square}{18}$
5. $\frac{4}{5} = \frac{\square}{25}$
6. $\frac{9}{10} = \frac{\square}{100}$
7. $\frac{1}{5} = \frac{\square}{100}$
8. $\frac{2}{3} = \frac{\square}{15}$
9. $\frac{2}{5} = \frac{\square}{30}$
10. $\frac{1}{4} = \frac{\square}{60}$
11. $\frac{\square}{4} = \frac{9}{12}$
12. $\frac{\square}{5} = \frac{6}{15}$
13. $\frac{\square}{10} = \frac{35}{50}$
14. $\frac{\square}{6} = \frac{15}{18}$
15. $\frac{\square}{5} = \frac{60}{100}$
16. $\frac{\square}{7} = \frac{20}{35}$
17. $\frac{\square}{9} = \frac{8}{18}$
18. $\frac{\square}{3} = \frac{8}{12}$
19. $\frac{\square}{20} = \frac{40}{100}$
20. $\frac{\square}{8} = \frac{25}{40}$

On these pages you will learn to use letters in place of numbers.

Chris has many friends in other countries and likes to phone them each month.
He keep a check on the phone bill by using a simple code.

Example

3A would mean 3 minutes phoning America.

7C would mean 7 minutes phoning Canada.

The phone charges are as follows:

America	A	means	60 pence per minute
Belgium	B	means	30 pence per minute
Canada	C	means	80 pence per minute
Denmark	D	means	25 pence per minute
France	F	means	20 pence per minute
Germany	G	means	35 pence per minute
Holland	H	means	40 pence per minute
Jamaica	J	means	90 pence per minute

Example

3A = 3 × A = 3 × 60 = 180 pence or £1.80

7C = 7 × C = 7 × 80 = 560 pence or £5.60

2F + 3H means (2 × 20) + (3 × 40) = 40 + 120 = 160 pence = £1.60

M

Using this code, work out how much money Chris spent on phone calls in each of the following months:

1
Jan
2A
3B
4C

2
Feb
3A
B
5F

3
March
A
6H
4D

4
April
4B
3C
4G
6F

5
May
2D
2G
5J
6B

6
June
5A
4C
5J
3H

(7) *July*: 2D + 8C + 7B

(8) *Aug*: 10F + 5H + 6B + 4D

(9) *Sept*: 4H + 7B + 4C + 8F + 2J

(13) Which month cost the least money?

(10) *Oct*: 3C + 4B + 2D + 6H + A

(11) *Nov*: A + 3C + 6D + 3G + J

(12) *Dec*: 5F + 7H + 8D + 6C + 2A

E

The phone charges are changed as follows:
Country Code Pence per minute

Country	Code	Pence per minute
America	A	62
Belgium	B	33
Canada	C	85
Denmark	D	27
France	F	28
Germany	G	38
Holland	H	45
Jamaica	J	92

Example

The code for 5 minutes to Belgium, 8 minutes to France and 9 minutes to Jamaica is 5B + 8F + 9J.

For Questions **1** to **5** below, write down the code:

1 8 minutes to America, 9 minutes to Germany and 6 minutes to Holland.

2 6 minutes to Canada, 12 minutes to France and 11 minutes to Holland.

3 10 minutes to Denmark, 8 minutes to France and 14 minutes to Jamaica.

4 15 minutes to Belgium, 9 minutes to Denmark, 11 minutes to Holland and 21 minutes to Jamaica.

5 8 minutes to Canada, 14 minutes to Germany, 23 minutes to Holland and 17 minutes to Jamaica.

Using the code and table above, work out how much money was spent on phone calls for each Question below:

6 3A + 9F

7 3B + 10C + 4H

8 5D + 6G + 4J

9 6C + 3F + 7H

10 10A + 5D + 6G + 10J

11 6B + 3F + 10G + 5H

12 9A + 10C + 5F + 8G

On these pages you will collect like terms and multiply out brackets.

Examples

1 $6a + 3b + 2b + 2a$

    $= 8a + 5b$

2 $5a + a + 2a$

    $= 8a$

Beware $3a + 8$ is *not* $11a$

$3a + 8$ *cannot* be simplified

M

Collect like terms

1 $5a + 2b + 2a$

2 $2a + 6b + a$

3 $4a + 2a + 3b$

4 $5p + 7q + 2p$

5 $8p + 3p + 4q$

6 $5p + 2q + 4p + 2q$

7 $7p + 3p + 2q + 3q$

8 $5p + 6q + p + q$

9 $8x + 4y - 2x$

10 $3x + 2x - 3x$

11 $4x + 6y - 3y$

12 $2a + 9a - 3a$

13 $8x + 3x + 2y$

14 $6x - 2x + 3x$

15 $9x - 4x + 3y$

16 $6a + 3b - 2a - b$

17 $7a + 2 + 5a - 1$

18 $6x - 1 + 4x - 3x$

19 $9p + 3q + 2q - 2p$

20 $8c + 4c - 1 + 2c$

21 $9a + 7b - 3a - 4b$

22 $5a + 7a + 4a + 7$

23 $3x + 2y + 3y - x$

24 $5c + 4 + 7 - 2c$

E

Find the perimeter of the following shapes:

1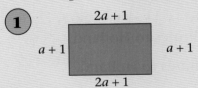

2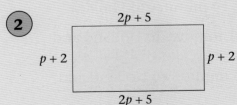

3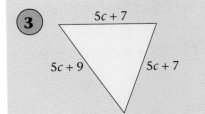

4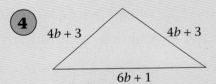

5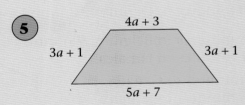

6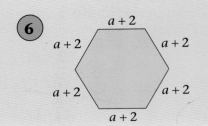

Substitution and Formulas 1

On these pages you will learn how to put numbers in place of letters in expressions and formulas.

$5a$ means $5 \times a$

ab means $a \times b$

a^2 means $a \times a$

$6a + 7$ means '$6 \times a$ then add 7'

$3(a - 2)$ means '$a - 2$ then multiply by 3'

$\frac{a}{b}$ means $a \div b$

An *expression* does *not* have an '=' sign.

Examples

$3a - 7$ $\qquad\qquad$ $2a + b$ $\qquad\qquad$ $ab + c$

These are all expressions.

Substitution

Find the value of each expression when $a = 3$, $b = 2$ and $c = 5$.

$ab = 3 \times 2 = 6$

$5a + 7 = 5 \times 3 + 7 = 15 + 7 = 22$

$c^2 = 5 \times 5 = 25$

$a(b + c) = 3 \times (2 + 5) = 3 \times 7 = 21$

$2b + c = 2 \times 2 + 5 = 4 + 5 = 9$

$\frac{a + c}{b} = \frac{8}{2} = 4$

Remember BODMAS. The order of operations is Brackets then $\div \times + -$.

Ⓜ

In Questions ① to ⑯ find the value of each expression when $a = 4$, $b = 2$ and $c = 3$.

① $7a$

② ab

③ bc

④ $4c$

⑤ $a - b$

⑥ $3a - b$

⑦ c^2

⑧ a^2

⑨ $a^2 + c^2$

⑩ $2a + 4c$

⑪ $5a - 3b$

⑫ $4(a + b)$

⑬ $b(a + c)$

⑭ $\frac{a}{b}$

⑮ $c(2a + 1)$

⑯ $\frac{2c}{b}$

In Questions ⑰ to ㉜ find the value of each expression when $x = 3$, $y = 5$ and $z = 1$.

⑰ $4y$

⑱ $5x$

⑲ $2z$

⑳ $5x + 4y$

㉑ $5y - 3z$

㉒ xy

㉓ xz

㉔ $\frac{x + y}{z}$

㉕ y^2

㉖ $x^2 + y^2$

㉗ $3(y + z)$

㉘ $6(2y - z)$

㉙ $z(3x + y)$

㉚ $y(2x + y)$

㉛ $5y - z^2$

㉜ $\frac{y - x}{2z}$

In Questions (33) to (44) find the value of each expression.

(33) $3x + 1$ if $x = 5$

(34) $5x - 2$ if $x = 2$

(35) $8x + 5$ if $x = 3$

(36) x^2 if $x = 4$

(37) $12 + a$ if $a = 6$

(38) $9 + 3c$ if $c = 4$

(39) $8 + 6d$ if $d = 3$

(40) $30 - 4c$ if $c = 7$

(41) $2(a + 6)$ if $a = 4$

(42) $a(a + 6)$ if $a = 3$

(43) $c^2 + 9$ if $c = 6$

(44) $a^2 - 8$ if $a = 7$

A formula is used to solve problems.

w

l

l is length

w is width

Area of rectangle = length × width

Let Area be A

then $A = l \times w$

we say $\boxed{A = lw}$ This is a formula.

Example

If length = 3 cm and width = 5 cm

then $l = 3$ and $w = 5$

so Area $A = lw$

so $A = 3 \times 5$

so $A = 15$

E

In Questions (1) to (10) use the formula $A = lw$ to find the area of each rectangle.

(1)

$w = 3$
$l = 6$

(2)
$w = 4$
$l = 5$

(6)
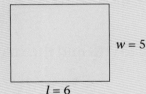
$w = 5$
$l = 6$

(7)

$w = 7$
$l = 10$

(3) length = 7, width = 5

(4) length = 9, width = 7

(5) $l = 8$, $w = 4$

(8) $l = 12$, $w = 8$

(9) $l = 20$, $w = 7$

(10) $l = 50$, $w = 20$

In Questions ⑪ to ⑯ use the formula $A = \dfrac{bh}{2}$ to find the area A of each triangle.

(This means 'work out $b \times h$ then divide by 2')

⑪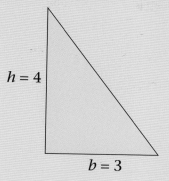

$h = 4$

$b = 3$

⑭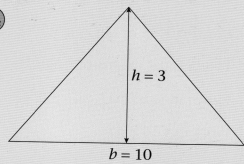

$h = 3$

$b = 10$

⑫ $b = 4, h = 4$

⑬ $b = 8, h = 6$

⑮ $b = 7, h = 6$

⑯ $b = 100, h = 4$

In Questions ⑰ to ㉒ use the formula $D = \dfrac{M}{V}$ to find the density D of a substance.
(M means Mass and V means Volume)

⑰ Mass = 40, Volume = 8

⑱ Mass = 80, Volume = 10

⑲ M = 50, V = 5

⑳ M = 60, V = 12

㉑ M = 150, V = 50

㉒ M = 105, V = 5

In Questions ㉓ to ㉘ use the formula $s = ut$ to find the value of s. (s means distance, u means speed and t means time taken)

㉓ $u = 3, t = 10$

㉔ $u = 9, t = 7$

㉕ $u = 7, t = 8$

㉖ $u = 12, t = 10$

㉗ $u = 17, t = 20$

㉘ $u = 19, t = 13$

In Questions ㉙ to ㉞ use the formula $v = at + u$ to find the value of v. (This means 'work out $a \times t$ then add u')

㉙ $a = 3, t = 9$ and $u = 10$

㉚ $a = 8, t = 4$ and $u = 20$

㉛ $a = 7, t = 9$ and $u = 38$

㉜ $a = 10, t = 12$ and $u = 41$

㉝ $a = 8, t = 15$ and $u = 73$

㉞ $a = 18, t = 24$ and $u = 127$

1 Subtract 174 from 726

2 Harry is 1.65 m tall.

Leena is 0.2 m shorter than Harry

How tall is Leena?

3 Work out 16×65

4 Work out $330 \div 55$

5 Write these temperatures in order, *coldest first.*

7°C   0°C   –3°C   18°C   –12°C

6 Look at these number cards:

+5	–3	+6
–6	+8	0

a) Choose a card to give the *highest* possible answer to the sum below.
Copy and fill in the card below then work out the answer.

–3	+		=

----

b) Choose a card to give the answer 5.

| +5 | + | –6 | + | | = 5 |

7

Shape 1

Shape 2

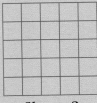

Shape 3

If this shape pattern continues, how many small squares will make shape 4?

8 Which is larger:

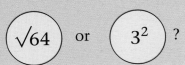

$\sqrt{64}$ or 3^2 ?

9 $2^3 = 8$ because 2^3 means $2 \times 2 \times 2$.

What is the value of 4^3?

10

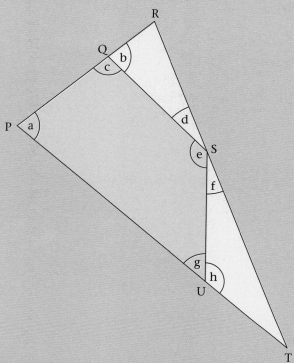

Angle RSQ is shown by the small letter d.

Angle QSU is shown by the small letter e.

Which angle is shown by the small letter h.

11 Look at these angles.

a) One of the angles measures 150º.

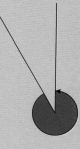

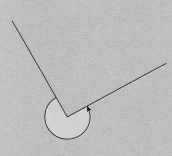

    angle A   angle B   angle C   angle D

Write its letter.

b) Copy the line below and use a protractor to complete the drawing to show an angle of 162°.

_____

12 I think of a rule.

The rule changes 12 to 6 and it changes 20 to 10.

$$12 \longrightarrow 6 \qquad 20 \longrightarrow 10$$

Write down what the rule could be.

13 Write down each expression in its *simplest* form.

a) $9 + 3p + 4p$

b) $m + 6 + 3m + 12$

14 When $x = 6$, work out the values of the expressions below.

a) $3x + 7$

b) $4x - 8$

c) $10 + 8x$

15 Find the value of angle x.

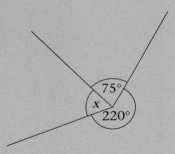

16 Find the values of angle y and angle z.

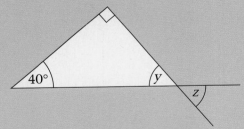

17 Find the value of angle m.

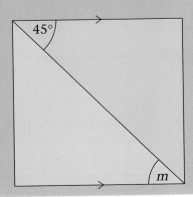

18 Find the *lowest common multiple* of 4 and 6 (i.e. find the lowest number in both the '4 times table' *and* the '6 times table').

19 Write down all the numbers below that are *factors of twelve*.

$$1 \quad 2 \quad 3 \quad 4 \quad 5 \quad 6$$
$$7 \quad 8 \quad 9 \quad 10 \quad 11 \quad 12$$

20 Look at this shape.

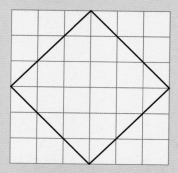

Copy the sentences below and fill in the gaps.

The shape has...........................right angles.

It has...........................straight sides.

It has...........................pairs of parallel sides.

...........................sides are the same length.

21 Sally and Pete are sister and brother. There are two bedrooms in their house as shown below.

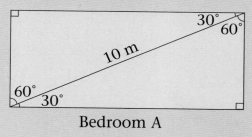

Bedroom A

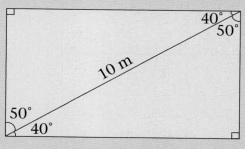

Bedroom B

They each want the bedroom with the larger area.

They toss a coin and Sally wins.

(a) Which bedroom does Sally choose? (You need to use a ruler and protractor to draw each bedroom using a scale of 1 cm to 1 m. Next use a calculator to work out each bedroom area with 'length × width'.)

(b) How much larger is the area of Sally's bedroom than Pete's bedroom?

On this page you will read number messages.

Instructions:-

1. Start in the box marked X.

2. Work out the answer to the question at the bottom of the box.

3. Find the box which has the answer in the top right hand corner.

4. Write down the letter in this box. Now work out the answer to the question in that box.

5. Look for the answer as in **3**. Don't forget to record the letter!

6. Continue this process until you arrive back at box X.

7. Read the message.

1

100 X $8+17$	61 A $77+12$	40 U $21+35$	62 D $27+33$	71 F $37+22$
25 O $63+8$	4 G $49+51$	70 N $2+2$	89 N $45+17$	23 S $14+17$
91 N $38+25$	60 R $12+19$	88 P $16+75$	22 O $16+24$	56 R $17+8$
27 H $27+24$	52 I $21+49$	31 U $82+9$	99 B $48+33$	85 J $65+33$
20 Y $13+9$	3 W $12+80$	59 F $28+33$	63 N $37+15$	17 A $27+11$

2

100 X $27-19$	48 B $25-16$	26 W $19-8$	29 A $51-17$	22 O $81-40$
16 A $47-29$	31 R $50-30$	17 T $65-43$	43 S $80-17$	5 U $27-11$
39 N $42-13$	46 O $13-8$	1 A $101-1$	28 E $98-81$	15 H $60-19$
41 P $75-27$	40 L $71-70$	70 G $43-24$	38 M $16-7$	77 N $71-42$
99 Q $43-29$	9 A $94-17$	18 R $41-13$	34 N $2-1$	8 Y $66-20$

3

100 X 3×5	41 B 3×2	24 O 2×9	42 A 7×8	27 C 7×7
81 C 6×7	32 A 2×8	51 S 7×4	83 T 6×8	21 K 7×9
20 E 3×10	14 R 3×8	56 L 3×9	7 E 2×7	45 O 1×1
15 L 6×4	49 U 10×5	18 O 3×7	16 T 5×9	1 R 10×10
64 O 9×9	72 P 10×9	90 H 9×8	50 L 4×8	63 N 8×8

4

100 X $20\div5$	20 E $9\div3$	5 T $49\div7$	21 H $8\div4$	14 A $39\div3$
12 A $99\div9$	16 M $21\div3$	3 H $15\div15$	18 C $51\div17$	11 B $20\div10$
9 G $3\div1$	13 S $60\div5$	15 T $30\div6$	8 R $12\div2$	7 O $70\div7$
10 N $100\div1$	4 B $24\div3$	19 P $81\div3$	20 E $57\div3$	21 D $30\div5$
1 T $28\div2$	25 Y $100\div50$	17 S $99\div3$	2 U $30\div2$	6 I $90\div10$

5

100 X 12×7	19 I 9×9	96 E $18\div3$	6 P 12×8	81 S 7×8
95 S $54+7$	144 D 10×10	121 F $84\div7$	61 R 7×5	116 T $43-17$
84 O $20\div4$	91 R $71-49$	29 Y 0×7	0 C $32-7$	22 L 12×12
12 T $38+47$	35 A $2\div1$	26 O 11×11	9 O $49+42$	8 H $16\div4$
56 W $72\div8$	37 U $22+7$	5 U $67+49$	10 I 8×5	85 H $58-39$

Ordering Fractions

On this page you will use your knowledge of equivalent fractions to compare and order fractions.

Example

Place $\frac{5}{12}$, $\frac{1}{3}$, $\frac{1}{2}$ in order, smallest first.

Convert the fractions to a common denominator. $\frac{1}{3} = \frac{4}{12}$ $\frac{1}{2} = \frac{6}{12}$

Arrange in order. $\frac{1}{3}$, $\frac{5}{12}$, $\frac{1}{2}$

M

$$\frac{4}{10} \qquad \frac{5}{8} \qquad \frac{3}{6} \qquad \frac{6}{10}$$

$$\frac{4}{8} \qquad \frac{2}{6} \qquad \frac{7}{12} \qquad \frac{2}{5}$$

Which of the fractions in the box are:

(1) equal to one half?

(2) less than one half?

(3) greater than one half?

(4) Match the fractions to the letters.

$\frac{1}{2}$

$\frac{2}{5}$

$\frac{7}{10}$

$\frac{18}{20}$

$\frac{10}{100}$

— 1
— E
— D
— C
— B
— A
— 0

(5) Write down the larger fraction.

a) $\frac{1}{2}$ or $\frac{1}{3}$

b) $\frac{3}{4}$ or $\frac{3}{8}$

c) $\frac{1}{10}$ or $\frac{1}{5}$

E

Place in order, smallest first.

(1) $\frac{3}{4}$, $\frac{1}{2}$, $\frac{3}{8}$

(2) $\frac{1}{3}$, $\frac{1}{2}$, $\frac{1}{6}$

(3) $\frac{3}{5}$, $\frac{1}{2}$, $\frac{7}{10}$

(4) $\frac{11}{16}$, $\frac{3}{4}$, $\frac{5}{8}$

(5) $\frac{2}{3}$, $\frac{5}{6}$, $\frac{9}{12}$

(6) $\frac{2}{5}$, $\frac{5}{10}$, $\frac{9}{20}$

(7) Match the fractions to the letters.

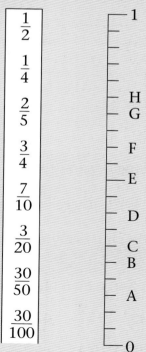

$\frac{1}{2}$

$\frac{1}{4}$

$\frac{2}{5}$

$\frac{3}{4}$

$\frac{7}{10}$

$\frac{3}{20}$

$\frac{30}{50}$

$\frac{30}{100}$

— 1
— H
— G
— F
— E
— D
— C
— B
— A
— 0

On these pages you will change decimals into fractions and fractions into decimals.

M

Change the following decimals into fractions:

1 0.1	**8** 0.06	**15** 0.45
2 0.3	**9** 0.03	**16** 0.137
3 0.5	**10** 0.07	**17** 0.241
4 0.7	**11** 0.15	**18** 0.373
5 0.9	**12** 0.37	**19** 0.479
6 0.05	**13** 0.69	**20** 0.507
7 0.04	**14** 0.83	

21 Copy this diagram *five* times:

For each of Questions **1** to **5** above shade in a diagram to show your answer.

Change the following fractions into decimals:

22 $\frac{1}{2}$	**26** $\frac{1}{4}$	**30** $\frac{47}{100}$
23 $\frac{3}{4}$	**27** $\frac{3}{100}$	**31** $\frac{23}{100}$
24 $\frac{1}{10}$	**28** $\frac{7}{10}$	
25 $\frac{8}{10}$	**29** $\frac{9}{100}$	

32 Which is larger, 0.18 or $\frac{13}{100}$?

33 Which is larger, $\frac{33}{100}$ or 0.29?

Change the following decimals into fractions:

34 0.01	**37** 0.02	**40** 0.67
35 0.93	**38** 0.177	**41** 0.199
36 0.81	**39** 0.003	

E

Use division to change the following fractions into decimals. Do not use a calculator.

1 $\frac{1}{5}$	**5** $\frac{9}{10}$	**9** $\frac{2}{5}$
2 $\frac{3}{10}$	**6** $\frac{4}{5}$	**10** $\frac{7}{20}$
3 $\frac{3}{5}$	**7** $\frac{3}{8}$	**11** $\frac{3}{100}$
4 $\frac{7}{10}$	**8** $\frac{7}{8}$	**12** $\frac{7}{50}$

You may use a calculator to change the following fractions into decimals.

13 $\frac{9}{15}$	**16** $\frac{7}{35}$	**19** $\frac{5}{16}$
14 $\frac{4}{25}$	**17** $\frac{11}{50}$	**20** $\frac{9}{200}$
15 $\frac{12}{15}$	**18** $\frac{13}{40}$	

For each question below, use a calculator to find out which 2 fractions are equal to each other.

21

$$\frac{7}{15} \qquad \frac{11}{20} \qquad \frac{33}{60} \qquad \frac{3}{5} \qquad \frac{6}{25}$$

22

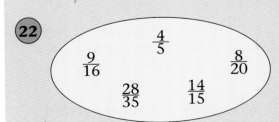

23 Which is greater, 0.4 or $\frac{3}{8}$?

24 Which is greater, $\frac{7}{16}$ or 0.4?

On these pages you will learn how to add and subtract fractions.

Hannah eats one third of a cake.

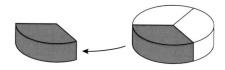

Joe eats one third of the cake.

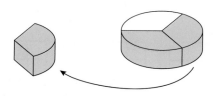

Together Hannah and Joe have eaten two-thirds of the cake.

One-third + one-third = two thirds

$$\frac{1}{3} \quad + \quad \frac{1}{3} \quad = \quad \frac{2}{3}$$

NEVER add the denominators (bottom numbers)

The denominators must be the same before adding.

Examples

$\frac{1}{5} + \frac{2}{5} = \frac{3}{5}$ → add the numerators (top numbers)
→ denominator (bottom number) stays same.

$\frac{2}{7} + \frac{3}{7} = \frac{5}{7}$

$\frac{5}{10} - \frac{2}{10} = \frac{3}{10}$ → subtract the numerators
→ denominator stays same

$\frac{8}{9} - \frac{1}{9} = \frac{7}{9}$

Ⓜ

Work out

(1) $\frac{1}{5} + \frac{2}{5}$ **(4)** $\frac{1}{8} + \frac{3}{8}$ **(7)** $\frac{3}{11} + \frac{2}{11}$

(2) $\frac{2}{7} + \frac{1}{7}$ **(5)** $\frac{2}{9} + \frac{3}{9}$ **(8)** $\frac{1}{25} + \frac{2}{25}$

(3) $\frac{1}{6} + \frac{4}{6}$ **(6)** $\frac{3}{10} + \frac{4}{10}$ **(9)** $\frac{4}{7} + \frac{2}{7}$

(10) Mrs. Thomas gave $\frac{5}{11}$ of her money to Janet and $\frac{4}{11}$ of her money to Chad. In total, what fraction of her money did she give away?

(11) Ben ate $\frac{3}{5}$ of his sweets and gave $\frac{1}{5}$ of his sweets to Helen who ate them immediately. What total fraction of his sweets has been eaten?

Work out

(12) $\frac{8}{9} - \frac{3}{9}$ **(15)** $\frac{5}{9} - \frac{1}{9}$ **(18)** $\frac{9}{10} - \frac{2}{10}$

(13) $\frac{4}{5} - \frac{1}{5}$ **(16)** $\frac{7}{8} - \frac{6}{8}$ **(19)** $\frac{9}{11} - \frac{7}{11}$

(14) $\frac{6}{7} - \frac{2}{7}$ **(17)** $\frac{8}{11} - \frac{5}{11}$ **(20)** $\frac{11}{20} - \frac{8}{20}$

In Questions **(21)** to **(23)**, which answer is the odd one out?

(21) a) $\frac{3}{5} + \frac{1}{5}$ b) $\frac{2}{5} + \frac{2}{5}$ c) $\frac{1}{5} + \frac{2}{5}$

(22) a) $\frac{3}{11} + \frac{3}{11}$ b) $\frac{8}{11} - \frac{2}{11}$ c) $\frac{5}{11} + \frac{2}{11}$

(23) a) $\frac{6}{7} - \frac{3}{7}$ b) $\frac{6}{7} - \frac{2}{7}$ c) $\frac{2}{7} + \frac{1}{7}$

Work out

(24) $\frac{3}{11} + \frac{2}{11} + \frac{4}{11}$ **(27)** $\frac{4}{8} + \frac{3}{8} - \frac{2}{8}$

(25) $\frac{5}{9} + \frac{1}{9} + \frac{2}{9}$ **(28)** $\frac{7}{12} + \frac{4}{12} - \frac{10}{12}$

(26) $\frac{2}{7} + \frac{2}{7} + \frac{1}{7}$ **(29)** $\frac{13}{20} + \frac{6}{20} - \frac{8}{20}$

Does $\frac{1}{4} + \frac{1}{8} = \frac{2}{12}$?

$$\frac{1}{4} \qquad + \qquad \frac{1}{8} \qquad = \qquad \frac{3}{8}$$

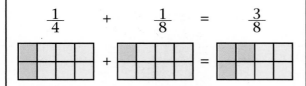

To do this sum without using pictures, the denominators (bottom numbers) must be made the same. Use equivalent fractions.

So $\left(\frac{1}{4}\right) + \frac{1}{8} = \left(\frac{2}{8}\right) + \frac{1}{8} = \frac{3}{8}$ ← remember: do *not* add the denominators.

Examples

$\left(\frac{1}{2}\right) + \frac{1}{4} = \left(\frac{2}{4}\right) + \frac{1}{4} = \frac{3}{4}$

$\frac{1}{6} + \left(\frac{1}{3}\right) = \frac{1}{6} + \left(\frac{2}{6}\right) = \frac{3}{6}$

$\frac{5}{8} - \left(\frac{1}{4}\right) = \frac{5}{8} - \left(\frac{2}{8}\right) = \frac{3}{8}$

E

Copy and complete the diagrams below to find the answers to the fraction questions.

1

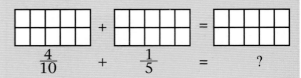

$$\frac{4}{10} \qquad + \qquad \frac{1}{5} \qquad = \qquad ?$$

2

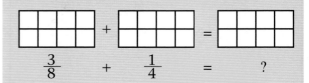

$$\frac{3}{8} \qquad + \qquad \frac{1}{4} \qquad = \qquad ?$$

3

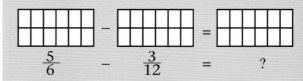

$$\frac{5}{6} \qquad - \qquad \frac{3}{12} \qquad = \qquad ?$$

Work out

4 $\frac{1}{4} + \frac{1}{2}$ **10** $\frac{1}{4} - \frac{1}{8}$ **16** $\frac{7}{8} - \frac{1}{2}$

5 $\frac{1}{8} + \frac{1}{4}$ **11** $\frac{5}{8} - \frac{1}{2}$ **17** $\frac{2}{3} - \frac{1}{6}$

6 $\frac{3}{8} + \frac{1}{2}$ **12** $\frac{1}{6} + \frac{2}{3}$ **18** $\frac{1}{10} - \frac{1}{20}$

7 $\frac{1}{16} + \frac{1}{2}$ **13** $\frac{4}{5} + \frac{1}{10}$ **19** $\frac{3}{4} - \frac{3}{8}$

8 $\frac{3}{4} - \frac{1}{2}$ **14** $\frac{2}{5} + \frac{3}{10}$

9 $\frac{5}{8} - \frac{1}{4}$ **15** $\frac{1}{6} + \frac{1}{3}$

20 Which answer below is the odd one out?

(a) $\frac{2}{12} + \frac{2}{6}$ (b) $\frac{4}{6} - \frac{1}{12}$ (c) $\frac{5}{6} - \frac{4}{12}$

Fractions of Quantities

On this page you will learn to find a fraction of a number or quantity.

Examples

$\frac{1}{8}$ of 640 = 640 ÷ 8
= 80

$\frac{1}{5}$ of 40 = 40 ÷ 5
= 8

$\frac{3}{10}$ of 90 = (90 ÷ 10) × 3
= 9 × 3 = 27

Find $\frac{1}{10}$ of:

(1) 30
(2) 80
(3) 20
(4) 50

(5) 70 cm
(6) 1 m
(7) 40p
(8) £1.00

Find $\frac{1}{3}$ of:

(17) 9
(18) 15
(19) 21
(20) 12

(21) 18 cm
(22) 27 cm
(23) 30p
(24) 24p

Find

(33) $\frac{1}{10}$ of 400
(34) $\frac{3}{10}$ of 70
(35) $\frac{3}{5}$ of 45
(36) $\frac{9}{10}$ of 60
(37) $\frac{1}{10}$ of 350
(38) $\frac{1}{6}$ of 42
(39) $\frac{1}{5}$ of 1 m
(40) $\frac{3}{4}$ of 48 cm
(41) $\frac{7}{10}$ of 1 m
(42) $\frac{2}{3}$ of 75p

Find $\frac{1}{5}$ of:

(9) 10
(10) 30
(11) 25
(12) 45

(13) 15 cm
(14) 50 cm
(15) 40p
(16) 35p

Find $\frac{1}{4}$ of:

(25) 8
(26) 32
(27) 24
(28) 36

(29) 16 cm
(30) 28 cm
(31) 40p
(32) 20p

Remember.

Find $\frac{3}{5}$ of 30

Answer: $\frac{1}{5}$ of 30 = 30 ÷ 5 = 6

So $\frac{3}{5}$ of 30 = 6 × 3 = 18

Example

Work out $\frac{2}{3}$ × 18

Answer: $\frac{2}{3}$ × 18 means $\frac{2}{3}$ of 18

$\frac{1}{3}$ of 18 = 18 ÷ 3 = 6

and $\frac{2}{3}$ of 18 = 6 × 2 = 12

so $\frac{2}{3}$ × 18 = 12.

> 'of' means '×'
>
> $\frac{3}{5}$ of 30 can be written as $\frac{3}{5}$ × 30

Your teacher may wish to teach you the 'cancelling' way.

Sometimes it is easier to work out multiplication by cancelling.

Examples

a) $\frac{5}{\cancel{9}_{3}} \times \cancel{12}^{4} = \frac{20}{3}$
$= 6\frac{2}{3}$

b) $\frac{3}{\cancel{8}_{2}} \times \cancel{12}^{3} = \frac{9}{2}$
$= 4\frac{1}{2}$

c) $\frac{5}{\cancel{12}_{4}} \times \cancel{15}^{5} = \frac{25}{4}$
$= 6\frac{1}{4}$

E

Copy and complete these problems. (Use a calculator if needed)

1 $\frac{3}{8}$ of £24 = ?

2 $\frac{2}{5}$ of £15 = ?

3 $\frac{3}{4}$ of £36 = ?

4 $\frac{4}{7}$ of £84 = ?

5 $\frac{5}{9}$ of £108 = ?

6 $\frac{2}{3}$ of £216 = ?

7 $\frac{3}{4}$ of 20 kg = ?

8 $\frac{2}{3}$ of 30 kg = ?

9 $\frac{7}{10}$ of 30 g = ?

10 $\frac{5}{8}$ of 480 cm = ?

11 $\frac{4}{5}$ of 80 cm = ?

12 $\frac{2}{3}$ of 120 cm = ?

13 $\frac{2}{5}$ of 30 p = ?

14 $\frac{5}{8}$ of 64 p = ?

15 $\frac{3}{10}$ of 150 p = ?

16 $\frac{2}{7}$ of 140 m = ?

17 $\frac{5}{12}$ of 60 km = ?

18 $\frac{8}{9}$ of 72 litres = ?

19 In a maths test full marks were 120. How many marks did Ben get if he got $\frac{7}{10}$ of full marks?

20 A petrol tank in a car holds 56 litres when full. How much petrol is in the tank when it is $\frac{3}{4}$ full?

21 A rose garden is home to 2600 ladybirds. If $\frac{3}{100}$ of these are male, how many females are there?

22 Mario has an order for 600 pizzas. If $\frac{5}{12}$ of his pizzas must be vegetarian, how many will be non-vegetarian?

Work out

23 $\frac{1}{2} \times 8$

24 $\frac{1}{4} \times 28$

25 $\frac{1}{3} \times 60$

26 $\frac{1}{4} \times 20$

27 $\frac{1}{2} \times 16$

28 $\frac{1}{3} \times 27$

Copy and complete the following questions:

29 $\frac{5}{\underset{2}{8}} \times \overset{3}{\cancel{12}} = \frac{\square}{\square} = \square$

30 $\frac{3}{\underset{1}{7}} \times \overset{2}{\cancel{14}} = \frac{\square}{\square} = \square$

31 $\frac{5}{\underset{3}{12}} \times \frac{\overset{4}{\cancel{16}}}{1} = \frac{\square}{\square} = \square$

32 $\frac{2}{\underset{3}{9}} \times \frac{\overset{5}{\cancel{15}}}{1} = \frac{\square}{\square} = \square$

33 If a book has 440 pages and you have read $\frac{3}{8}$ so far, how many more pages do you still have to read?

34 Here are calculations with letters. Put the answers in order of size, smallest first. Write down the letters to make a word.

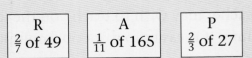

R	A	P
$\frac{2}{7}$ of 49	$\frac{1}{11}$ of 165	$\frac{2}{3}$ of 27

M	Y	D	I
$\frac{4}{9}$ of 45	$\frac{3}{4}$ of 16	$\frac{5}{6}$ of 300	$\frac{5}{8}$ of 96

On these pages you will learn to find percentages of numbers.

Examples

a) 10% of 50

   $= \frac{1}{10}$ of 50

   $= 50 \div 10$

   $= 5$

b) 30% of 60

   FIND 10% FIRST

   10% of 60 = $\boxed{6}$

   3 × 10% GIVES 30%

   30% of 60 = $\boxed{6}$ × 3

   $\qquad = 18$

c) 5% of 40

   FIND 10% FIRST

   10% of 40 = $\boxed{4}$

   5% IS HALF OF 10%

   5% of 40 = $\frac{1}{2}$ of $\boxed{4}$

   $\qquad = 2$

d) 10% of 45

   $= \frac{1}{10}$ of 45

   $= 45 \div 10$

   $= 4.5$

M

Work out

1) 10% of 60

2) 10% of 70

3) 10% of 80

4) 10% of 90

5) 10% of 150

6) 10% of 160

7) 10% of 700

8) 10% of 800

9) 10% of 65

10) 10% of 85

11) 20% of 60

12) 20% of 70

13) 20% of 80

14) 20% of 90

15) 20% of 150

16) 30% of 60

17) 30% of 70

18) 30% of 80

19) 30% of 90

20) 30% of 150

21) 10% of 25

22) 20% of 25

23) 10% of 55

24) 20% of 55

25) 10% of 86

26) 10% of 71

27) 20% of 700

28) 30% of 120

29) 30% of 250

30) 60% of 70

31) Copy and complete the table.

Money (€)	10%	5%	$2\frac{1}{2}$%	$17\frac{1}{2}$%
80	8	4	2	14
120				
300				
240				
440				
280				
84				
68				

E

Work out

1 1% of 300	**9** 1% of 66	**17** 2% of 720	**25** 7% of 200
2 1% of 500	**10** 1% of 78	**18** 2% of 840	**26** 1% of £112
3 1% of 900	**11** 2% of 300	**19** 3% of 66	**27** 4% of £2
4 1% of 400	**12** 2% of 500	**20** 3% of 78	**28** 9% of £700
5 1% of 700	**13** 3% of 900	**21** 1% of 46	**29** 12% of £300
6 1% of 360	**14** 6% of 400	**22** 1% of 69	**30** 23% of £400
7 1% of 720	**15** 6% of 700	**23** 2% of 28	
8 1% of 840	**16** 2% of 360	**24** 4% of 300	

31 Copy and complete the table.

Money (£)	10%	1%	4%	30%	34%
200	20	2	8	60	68
700					
900					
60					
80					
30					
1100					
1800					
64					
42					

32 Copy and complete the table.

640	10% = 64	20% = 128	2% = 12.8	32% =
280	10% =	30% =	3% =	43% =
160	10% =	40% =	4% =	54% =
330	10% =	1% =	3% =	14% =
740	10% =	20% =	2% =	32% =
1220	10% =	30% =	3% =	43% =
350	20% =	2% =	18% =	22% =
200	30% =	3% =	27% =	33% =
380	50% =	5% =	45% =	55% =
760	50% =	10% =	60% =	40% =
260	10% =	40% =	4% =	54% =

On these pages you will use percentages to increase and decrease numbers.

'increase' means 'make bigger'   'reduce' means 'make smaller'

'decrease' means 'make smaller'

Example

(a) Increase £60 by 10%.

FIND PERCENTAGE FIRST

10% of 60 = 6

Increase £60 by £6

Answer = 60 ⊞ 6

= £66

(b) Reduce £80 by 5%,

FIND PERCENTAGE FIRST.

10% of 80 = 8

so 5% of 80 = 4

Reduce £80 by £4

Answer = 80 ⊟ 4

= £76

Ⓜ

Ⓐ Increase £80 by 10%.

Ⓑ Increase £60 by 30%.

Ⓒ Increase £90 by 20%.

Ⓓ Decrease £40 by 25%.

Ⓔ Decrease £220 by 5%.

Ⓕ Increase £20 by 5%.

Ⓖ Reduce £300 by 30%.

Ⓗ Reduce £820 by 20%.

Ⓘ Decrease £45 by 50%.

Ⓙ Decrease £75 by 10%.

For each of the following items in a sale, find:

a) the amount the price is reduced.

b) the new price.

Ⓚ SUITS £100.00
10% OFF

Ⓛ GLOVES £5.00
50% OFF

Ⓜ SOCKS £2.40
25% OFF

Ⓝ BELTS £8.50
10% OFF

Ⓞ TROUSERS £15.00
20% OFF

Ⓟ TIES £3.60
10% OFF

Ⓠ TRAINERS £20.00
30% OFF

Ⓡ HATS £8
20% OFF

Ⓢ COATS £40.00
25% OFF

Ⓣ SHIRTS £10.00
40% OFF

Ⓤ SHOES £25.00
20% OFF

Ⓥ SCARVES £6.00
25% OFF

A shop adds 5% to the bill if goods are delivered to the home.

For each of the following items, find:

(a) the 5% delivery charge.　　(b) the total bill.

(23) Chairs costing £150.

(24) Garden seat costing £30.

(25) Swing chair costing £200.

(26) Lawn mower costing £82.

(27) Summer house costing £600.

(28) Hammock costing £26.

(29) Paint costing £48.

(30) Ladder costing £88.

When numbers are 'tricky', use a calculator.

Example

a) Find 27% of £6300

　　FIND 1% ➡ ÷ 100

　　THEN 27% ➡ × 27

Answer:

6300 ÷ 100 × 27 = £1701.

b) Find 79% of £82.

　　FIND 1% ➡ ÷ 100

　　THEN 79% ➡ × 79

Answer:

82 ÷ 100 × 79 = £64.78.

c) Increase £82 by 64%.

FIND PERCENTAGE FIRST.

64% of 82

USE CALCULATOR

82 ÷ 100 × 64 = 52.48

Increase £82 by £52.48

Answer = 82 + 52.48

　　　　= £134.48

E

Use a calculator to work out.

(1) 12% of £7700

(2) 16% of £4900

(3) 23% of £8500

(4) 47% of £7200

(5) 18% of £3500

(6) 76% of £18

(7) 14% of £79

(8) 36% of £26

(9) 27% of £15

(10) 52% of £125

(11) 34% of £1270

(12) 29% of £1530

(13) Increase £1500 by 17%.

(14) Increase £628 by 8%.

(15) Reduce £4300 by 33%.

(16) Decrease £7100 by 14%.

(17) Decrease £29 by 69%.

(18) Increase £78 by 47%.

19 A car dealer cuts prices by 6%.

Copy and complete the table to show the new prices.

Car	Price (£)	6% cut	New Price
Mini	6500		
BMW 5 Series	7900		
Audi Quattro Sport	8800		
Leyland Discovery	17 000		
Volvo V70 Estate	11 500		
VW Polo	7700		

20 Prices rise by 3%.

Copy and complete the table to show the new prices.

Item	Price (£)	3% rise	New Price
Fridge	375		
Toaster	45		
Calculator	9		
CD Player	92		
Hair Dryer	19		

21 62 500 people attended a football match between Manchester United and Arsenal. In their next game, 8% *more* people go to the match. How many people go to this match?

22 Albert earns £16 400 each year. He gets a pay rise of 12%. How much does he earn each year now?

23 A hair salon reduced prices to attract new customers.

Copy and complete the table below to show the new prices.

Item	Old Price (£)	Reduction	New Price
Trim Shampoo and Set	9	4% =	
Shampoo and Set	8	4% =	
Cut and Dry	15	5% =	
Whole Head Shampoo and Set	39	6% =	
$\frac{1}{2}$ Head Shampoo and Set	31	4% =	
Tint Shampoo and Set	18	12% =	
Highlight Shampoo and Set	37	8% =	

Multiplication and Division Facts

On this page you will practise multiplying and dividing.

Ⓜ

Write the answers only.

(1) 3 × 2   **(17)** 1 × 4   **(33)** 35 ÷ 5

(2) 8 × 2   **(18)** 8 × 4   **(34)** 50 ÷ 5

(3) 9 × 2   **(19)** 6 × 5   **(35)** 25 ÷ 5

(4) 0 × 2   **(20)** 8 × 5   **(36)** 40 ÷ 5

(5) 7 × 2   **(21)** 5 × 5   **(37)** 60 ÷ 10

(6) 6 × 2   **(22)** 3 × 5   **(38)** 80 ÷ 10

(7) 10 × 3   **(23)** 10 × 5   **(39)** 40 ÷ 10

(8) 6 × 3   **(24)** 7 × 5   **(40)** 70 ÷ 10

(9) 7 × 3   **(25)** 21 ÷ 3   **(41)** 100 ÷ 10

(10) 9 × 3   **(26)** 15 ÷ 3   **(42)** 90 ÷ 10

(11) 4 × 3   **(27)** 18 ÷ 3   **(43)** 36 ÷ 4

(12) 8 × 3   **(28)** 24 ÷ 3   **(44)** 24 ÷ 4

(13) 5 × 4   **(29)** 9 ÷ 3   **(45)** 16 ÷ 4

(14) 7 × 4   **(30)** 27 ÷ 3   **(46)** 32 ÷ 4

(15) 9 × 4   **(31)** 45 ÷ 5   **(47)** 40 ÷ 4

(16) 6 × 4   **(32)** 20 ÷ 5   **(48)** 28 ÷ 4

(49) Copy and complete the multiplication square.

×	9	3	7
6			
8			
4			

Copy and complete the tables.

(50)

÷ 6
30 → 5
54 →
→ 6
24 →
48 →
→ 7

(51)

÷ 7
21 → 3
56 →
→ 5
→ 9
28 →
49 →

(52)

÷ 8
16 → 2
64 →
→ 7
24 →
→ 9
→ 6

(53)

÷ 9
90 → 10
36 →
→ 9
18 →
54 →
→ 8

Copy and complete.

1 $81 \div \square = 9$

2 $77 \div \square = 7$

3 $5 \div \square = 0.5$

4 $\square \div 8 = 6$

5 $\square \div 6 = 7$

6 $54 \div \square = 6$

7 $120 \div \square = 6$

8 $14 \div \square = 14$

9 $\square \div 8 = 25$

10 $\square \div 5 = 9$

11 $100 \div \square = 5$

12 $24 \div \square = 2.4$

13 $80 \div \square = 20$

14 $\square \div 10 = 8.5$

15 $\square \div 1 = 8$

16 $500 \div \square = 10$

17 $30 \div \square = 2$

18 $15 \div \square = 1.5$

19 $\square \div 15 = 8$

20 $\square \div 12 = 6$

For each statement write three related × or ÷ statements.

For example:

$8 \times 6 = 48 \qquad 6 \times 8 = 48$
$48 \div 6 = 8 \qquad 48 \div 8 = 6$

21 $72 \div 12 = 6$

22 $5 \times 15 = 75$

23 $96 \div 6 = 16$

24 $21 \times 8 = 168$

25 $7 \times 19 = 133$

Copy and complete the tables.

26

× 6
4 → 24
8 →
6 →
1 →
→ 30
→ 0
→ 42
→ 54

27

× 7
6 → 42
0 →
7 →
9 →
→ 56
→ 28
→ 7
→ 35

28

× 8
8 → 64
0 →
5 →
4 →
→ 8
→ 48
→ 72
→ 56

29

× 9
5 → 45
7 →
9 →
10 →
→ 36
→ 72
→ 0
→ 54

Mental Strategies 1 (× and ÷)

On this page you will practise multiplying and dividing by 10, 100 or 1000.

Examples

50 × 200 = 10 000   70 × 600 = 42 000   6400 ÷ 100 = 64   2000 ÷ 1000 = 2

13 × 10 = 130   5100 ÷ 10 = 510

M

Multiply by 10.

(**1**) 35   (**5**) 269

(**2**) 52   (**6**) 386

(**3**) 81   (**7**) 67

(**4**) 174   (**8**) 290

Divide by 10.

(**9**) 2000   (**13**) 3000

(**10**) 400   (**14**) 5000

(**11**) 7000   (**15**) 600

(**12**) 800   (**16**) 9000

Multiply by 100.

(**17**) 27   (**21**) 51

(**18**) 64   (**22**) 8

(**19**) 7   (**23**) 90

(**20**) 46   (**24**) 38

Divide by 100.

(**25**) 6000   (**29**) 4000

(**26**) 200   (**30**) 8000

(**27**) 1000   (**31**) 300

(**28**) 900   (**32**) 7000

E

Work out

(**1**) 60 × 200   (**9**) 3000 ÷ 10

(**2**) 70 × 300   (**10**) 5800 ÷ 100

(**3**) 30 × 400   (**11**) 4000 ÷ 1000

(**4**) 70 × 500   (**12**) 6200 ÷ 10

(**5**) 30 × 800   (**13**) 9000 ÷ 100

(**6**) 40 × 900   (**14**) 5000 ÷ 1000

(**7**) 60 × 500   (**15**) 7600 ÷ 10

(**8**) 40 × 700   (**16**) 3000 ÷ 1000

Copy and complete.

(**17**) 60 × ☐ = 48 000

(**18**) 2700 ÷ ☐ = 27

(**19**) ☐ × 600 = 54 000

(**20**) ☐ ÷ 1000 = 9

(**21**) ☐ × 600 = 24 000

(**22**) 4300 ÷ ☐ = 430

(**23**) 60 × ☐ = 42 000

(**24**) ☐ ÷ 100 = 89

On this page you will practise doubling multiples of 5 and halving multiples of 10.

Examples

$145 × 2 = (100 × 2) + (40 × 2) + (5 × 2)$
$= 200 + 80 + 10$
$= 290$

$570 ÷ 2 = (500 ÷ 2) + (70 ÷ 2)$
$= 250 + 35$
$= 285$

M

Double these numbers.

(1)	15	(9)	30
(2)	20	(10)	55
(3)	40	(11)	35
(4)	25	(12)	80
(5)	45	(13)	110
(6)	60	(14)	90
(7)	95	(15)	75
(8)	65	(16)	130

Halve these numbers.

(17)	80	(25)	100
(18)	110	(26)	140
(19)	150	(27)	130
(20)	70	(28)	190
(21)	170	(29)	200
(22)	120	(30)	280
(23)	180	(31)	160
(24)	90	(32)	250

(33) The postbox is 270 metres from Lauren's house. How far does she walk when she posts a letter?

(34) How many pairs can be made from 500 socks?

E

Write the answers only.

(1)	270 × 2	(7)	270 ÷ 2
(2)	335 × 2	(8)	330 ÷ 2
(3)	175 × 2	(9)	490 ÷ 2
(4)	255 × 2	(10)	720 ÷ 2
(5)	360 × 2	(11)	850 ÷ 2
(6)	485 × 2	(12)	510 ÷ 2

Copy and complete.

(13) ☐ × 2 = 150

(14) ☐ ÷ 2 = 145

(15) ☐ × 2 = 530

(16) ☐ ÷ 2 = 290

(17) ☐ × 2 = 590

(18) ☐ ÷ 2 = 275

(19) ☐ × 2 = 950

(20) ☐ ÷ 2 = 355

(21) ☐ × 2 = 780

(22) ☐ ÷ 2 = 335

(23) ☐ × 2 = 370

(24) ☐ ÷ 2 = 165

(25) A prize of £560 is shared equally between the two winners. How much should each person receive?

On these pages you will practise a mixture of problems in your head using decimals, fractions and percentages.

Work out

(1) $\frac{1}{3}$ of 18

(2) $\frac{1}{4}$ of 28

(3) $\frac{1}{4}$ of 32

(4) $\frac{1}{5}$ of 30

(5) $\frac{1}{8}$ of 32

(6) 0.2 + 0.7

(7) 0.6 + 0.3

(8) 1.4 + 0.4

(9) 3.1 + 6.3

(10) 8.7 + 5.9

(11) £2.11 + £3.73

(12) £3.62 + £1.31

(13) £4.06 + £3.27

(14) £5.12 + £2.26

(15) £4.38 + £6.73

(16) $\frac{2}{3}$ of 18

(17) $\frac{3}{4}$ of 28

(18) $\frac{2}{5}$ of 30

(19) $\frac{3}{8}$ of 16

(20) $\frac{5}{6}$ of 42

(21) 8.9 – 3.6

(22) 4.6 – 2.1

(23) 7.6 – 3.4

(24) 8.6 – 5.2

(25) 6.1 – 2.9

(26) £1.86 – £1.43

(27) £3.64 – £1.51

(28) £6.83 – £4.52

(29) £3.16 – £1.09

(30) £2.41 – £2.36

(31) A painter buys three brushes for £5.25. He pays with a £10 note.

What change does he get?

(32) Which is larger?

20% of £80 or 50% of £40

(33) Which is larger?

10% of £70 or 5% of £120

(34) Which is larger?

70% of £30 or 5% of £200

(35) Which is larger?

30% of £10 or 25% of £8

Work out

(36) $\frac{1}{5} + \frac{2}{5}$

(37) $\frac{3}{10} + \frac{6}{10}$

(38) $\frac{5}{7} - \frac{4}{7}$

(39) $\frac{7}{9} - \frac{3}{9}$

(40) $\frac{8}{11} + \frac{2}{11}$

In Questions **(41)** to **(45)** change the number into a fraction.

(41) 0.8

(42) 0.07

(43) 17%

(44) 2%

(45) 0.17

In Questions **(46)** to **(50)** change the number into a decimal.

(46) $\frac{3}{10}$

(47) 7%

(48) $\frac{19}{100}$

(49) $\frac{3}{4}$

(50) 20%

E

1. 60% of the children in a class are boys. What percentage are girls?

2. 54% of the boys in Year 8 have a skateboard. What percentage of the boys do not have a skateboard?

3. John is given 30% of £80. How much money does he get?

4. Millie buys a book for £4.85. How much change does she get from £10?

5. Henry buys chocolate for £1.15 and a drink for £1.05. How much change does he get from £5?

6. Sophie saves £3.50 each week for ten weeks. How much money does she save in total?

7. Max has 21 cds. He gives $\frac{1}{3}$ of his cds to Jasmine. How many cds does he give to Jasmine?

8. Prini has 48 shells in her collection. She gives $\frac{1}{8}$ of them to her sister. How many shells does she have left?

9. Terry is offered $\frac{1}{5}$ of £40 or $\frac{2}{3}$ of £15. Which amount would give him the most money?

10. Two years ago Lee's height was 148 cm.
Now Lee's height is 1.7 metres. How much has Lee grown?

11. 60 pupils go to the gym club. 25% of them are girls. How many are boys?

12. In March, Jack plays 80 games of skittles. He wins 20% of the games. How many games does he win?

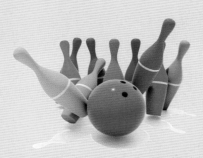

13. 120 people go to the cinema. 40% of them are male. How many are female?

14. Increase £20 by 10%.

15. Zoe earns £300 each week. She is given a 5% pay rise. How much extra money is she given each week?

16. Sam has £50. He loses 20% of his money. How much money does he have left?

17. Dan and Kelly have £25 between them. They spend £9.20 on some food and £3.50 on the bus. How much money do they have left?

On these pages you will learn how to work out the chance of certain events happening.

For simple events, like throwing a dice or tossing a coin, we can work out the expected probability of an event occurring.

For a fair dice the *expected probability* of throwing a '3' is $\frac{1}{6}$.

For a normal coin the expected probability of tossing a 'head' is $\frac{1}{2}$

> Expected probability = $\dfrac{\text{the number of ways the event can happen}}{\text{the number of possible outcomes}}$

Random choice: If a card is chosen at random from a pack, it means that every card has an equal chance of being chosen.

Nine identical discs numbered 1, 2, 3, 4, 5, 6, 7, 8, 9 are put into a bag. One disc is selected at random.

a) The probability of selecting a '4' = $\frac{1}{9}$

This may be written p (selecting a '4') = $\frac{1}{9}$

b) p (selecting an odd number) = $\frac{5}{9}$

c) p (selecting a number greater than 5) = $\frac{4}{9}$

Ⓜ

① A bag contains 2 red balls, 4 blue balls and a yellow ball. One ball is chosen at random. Copy and complete these sentences.

a) The probability that a red ball is chosen is … $\dfrac{\Box}{7}$

b) The probability that a blue ball is chosen is … $\dfrac{\Box}{\Box}$

c) The probability that the yellow ball is chosen is $\dfrac{\Box}{\Box}$

② A hat contains 3 white balls and 2 black balls.

One ball is chosen at random. Find the probability that it is

a) white   b) black.

Work out the probability of each of the following. Give each answer as a fraction.

(3) Rolling a dice and getting a 4.

(4) Rolling a dice and getting a 2.

(5) Rolling a dice and getting an even number.

(6) Rolling a dice and getting a 7.

(7) Rolling a dice and getting a number larger than 2.

(8) Spinning a coin and getting a head.

(9) Spinning a coin and getting a tail.

(10) A fishtank has 5 black fish and 3 white fish.

If I take out one fish, what is the probability of selecting

a) a white fish   b) a black fish   c) a goldfish.

E

(1) 7 balls numbered 1, 2, 3, 4, 5, 6, 7 are put into a bag. One ball is chosen at random.

Find the probability of

a) choosing a '3'   b) not choosing a '3'

(2) A set of snooker balls consists of 15 red balls, 1 yellow, 1 green, 1 brown, 1 blue, 1 pink, 1 black and 1 white.

If one ball is picked at random, find the probability of it being:

a) red   c) black

b) not red   d) not black

(3) 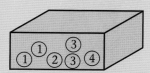   6 balls numbered 1, 1, 2, 3, 3, 4 are put into a box. One ball is chosen at random.

Find the probability of

a) choosing a '2'   b) not choosing a '2'.

4 A dice has its faces numbered 2, 3, 3, 3, 4, 7.
Find the probability of rolling

   a) a '7'   b) an even number.

5 One card is selected at random from the nine
cards shown.

Find the probability of selecting

   a) the ace of diamonds   b) a king

   c) an ace

6 The 26 letters of the alphabet are written on discs. The five discs with vowels are
put in bag A and the other discs are put in bag B.

Find the probability of selecting

   a) an 'o' from bag A

   b) a 'z' from bag B

   c) a 'w' from bag A

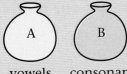

vowels   consonants

7 Nicole has 3 kings and 1 ace.
She shuffles the cards and takes
one without looking.

Nicole asks two of her friends
about the probability of getting
an ace

Angie says:

'It is $\frac{1}{3}$ because there are

3 kings and 1 ace.'

Syline says

'It is $\frac{1}{4}$ because there are

4 cards and only 1 ace.'

Which of her friends is right?

8 A field contains 10 cows, 5 horses and 1 puma.
The puma is thought to be tame and half of
the cows are mad.

One animal is chosen at random.
Find the probability that the animal:

   a) is mad

   b) enjoys eating grass

   c) might eat you.

On these pages you will collect data from a game and record it in a frequency table. You will use this data to estimate what will happen.

This is a game for 2 players, A and B (decide who is A and B).

Both players put one hand behind their back and make either:

(**1**) A closed fist (meant to be a stone)

(**2**) A victory 'V' sign (meant to be a pair of scissors)

(**3**) A flat hand (meant to be a sheet of paper)

On a count of 3, both players show their hands together.

When the players choose differently, a player wins as follows:

stone + scissors ('stone wins' – 'because stone blunts scissors')

stone + paper ('paper wins' – 'because paper can wrap the stone')

scissors + paper ('scissors wins' – 'because scissors can cut paper')

Play the game with your partner *30 times* and each record the result in a table like the one opposite:

	A	B	Winner
1			B
2			A
3			A
4	⋮	⋮	⋮
5	⋮	⋮	⋮

From your results make your own tally chart like the one below:

Choice	Times chosen	Total	Wins
	JHT JHT I	11	?
	JHT III	8	?
	JHT JHT I	11	?

Using your results and a calculator, *discuss with your teacher* (and maybe the whole class):

a) the probability of winning if you choose 'stone',

b) the probability of winning if you choose 'scissors',

c) the probability of winning if you choose 'paper',

d) if you played the game another 30 times would you expect to get the same results? Why do you think this?

This is a game for 2 players, A and B (decide who is A and B). You will need one dice and one coin between you. Each player rolls the dice and records the score. Each player tosses the coin in turn to decide the winner as follows:

1 If the coin comes down heads, the higher dice number wins.

2 If the coin comes down tails, the lower dice number wins.

3 If both numbers are the same, throw again until you have a win. Play the game with your partner until there are 30 wins in total. Record the results in a table like the one below:

Turn	A (dice)	B (dice)	Coin	Winning number
1	5	4	H	5
2	6	2	T	2
3	3	3	H or T	Throw again
⋮	⋮	⋮	⋮	⋮

From your results make your own tally chart like the one below:

Dice number	Player A		Player B		Player A + Player B	Number of times dice number wins
1	ⅧⅡ	(8)	ⅧⅧ	(9)	8 + 9 = 17	?
2	Ⅷ	(6)	Ⅲ	(3)	6 + 3 = 9	?
3	Ⅲ	(3)	Ⅷ	(5)	3 + 5 = 8	?
4	ⅧⅧ	(10)	ⅧⅧⅠ	(11)	10 + 11 = 21	?
5	Ⅲ	(2)	Ⅱ	(2)	2 + 2 = 4	?
6	Ⅰ	(1)		(0)	1 + 0 = 1	?

Using your results and a calculator *discuss with your teacher* (and maybe the whole class):

a) the probability of winning if you throw a '1'

b) the probability of winning if you throw a '2'

c) the probability of winning if you throw a '3'

d) the probability of winning if you throw a '4'

e) the probability of winning if you throw a '5'

f) the probability of winning if you throw a '6'

g) if you played the game for another 30 wins, would you expect to get the same results? Why do you think this?

On these pages you will list all the possible outcomes when two things happen.

Example

A mother has 2 children.

The first child could be a boy and the second child could be a boy or a girl.

1st child	2nd child	
boy	boy	
boy	girl	2 possible outcomes

The first child could be a girl and the second child could be a boy or a girl.

1st child	2nd child	
girl	boy	
girl	girl	2 possible outcomes

In total there are *4 possible outcomes*.

1st child	2nd child
boy	boy
boy	girl
girl	boy
girl	girl

Ⓜ

① A coin can land in two ways: head up (H) or tail up (T).

If a coin is thrown *twice*, list the 4 posssible outcomes. Copy and complete the table below to show your answers:

1st throw	2nd throw
H	H
	T
T	

2 For breakfast, Ron eats toast or an egg. He drinks tea or coffee. Copy and complete the table below to show all the different breakfasts he might have.

Food	Drink
toast	tea
	coffee
egg	

3 Ellie throws a coin and a dice. She could get a 'head' and a '5' (H 5). She could get a 'tail' and a '5' (T 5). List the 12 possible outcomes.

4 For lunch, Alana eats pizza or pasta and drinks coke or lemonade. Copy and complete the table below to show all the different lunches she might have.

Food	Drink
pizza	coke
pizza	

5 David wants to see 3 films at the cinema: 'Warrior Sims', 'The Holland Rings' and 'Dixon of Frome Green'.

David only has enough money to see 2 films. List all the pairs of films he might see. Start with 'Warrior Sims', 'The Holland Rings'. Now carry on.

6 On Monday, Joe plays tennis *or* football. On Tuesday he plays cricket *or* basketball. Copy and complete the table below to show what Joe might do on a Monday and Tuesday.

Monday	Tuesday
Tennis	Cricket
Tennis	

7 Sam goes to a pet shop to buy a dog and a cat. There are 2 dogs (a spaniel and a Labrador). There are 2 cats (a tabby and a manx).

List the pairs of dog and cat which Sam could buy. (Start with 'spaniel', 'tabby' then carry on.)

E

1 You may choose 2 pizza toppings from ham, mushroom and peppers.

List all the possible pairs of toppings you might choose (Start with 'ham', 'mushroom' then carry on).

2 Jack wears red or blue socks and blue or green trousers. Copy and complete the table below to show colours he might wear.

socks	trousers
red	blue
red	

3 Mindy uses a spinner (with the numbers 1, 2 and 3 on it) and a dice.

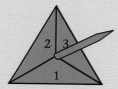

She could get a '2' with the spinner and a '4' with the dice (2, 4).

She could get a '2' with the spinner and a '5' with the dice (2, 5).

List the 18 possible outcomes.

4 2 dice are thrown. List all possible outcomes (there are 36 ways!)

Copy and complete:

(1, 1) (2, 1) (3, 1) (4, 1) (5, 1) (6, 1)

(1, 2) (2, 2) (3, 2) . . .   .

(1, 3) . . .   .

. . .   .

5 The four cards shown are shuffled and placed face down on a table.

Two cards are selected at random.

List all the possible pairs of cards which could be selected.

There are 6 possible pairs (e.g. 2, 6)

On these pages you will learn to convert one metric unit to another.

10 mm = 1 cm   100 cm = 1 m   1000 m = 1 km

Ⓜ

Copy and complete by writing the missing number in the box.

① 0 5 km = ☐ m   ⑦ 250 cm = ☐ m

② 0.6 km = ☐ m   ⑧ 140 cm = ☐ m

③ 1100 m = ☐ km   ⑨ 0.3 cm = ☐ mm

④ 3700 m = ☐ km   ⑩ 2.7 cm = ☐ mm

⑤ 1.5 m = ☐ cm   ⑪ 15 mm = ☐ cm

⑥ 0.8 m = ☐ cm   ⑫ 31 mm = ☐ cm

Suggest a suitable metric unit to measure these lengths.

⑬ a lollipop stick

⑭ a ladybird

⑮ the height of a block of flats

⑯ a pea

⑰ the Channel tunnel

⑱ a straw

Write the longer length from each pair.

⑲ 25 m   0.25 km

⑳ 33 mm   3 cm

㉑ 8 cm   0.8 m

㉒ 14.6 cm   46 mm

㉓ 600 m   6 km

㉔ 55 cm   0.5 m

㉕ One shelf is 65 cm long. Another shelf is 78 cm long. What is their total length in metres?

㉖ Lisa is 1.50 m tall. Shaun is 35 cm shorter. How tall is Shaun in metres?

㉗ Gary needs 10 pieces of ribbon. Each piece must be 50 cm long.
How many metres of ribbon does he need to buy?

㉘ A machine makes a staple from 20 mm of wire. How many staples will it make from 50 cm of wire?

㉙ Grace walks 80 m in one minute. How far does she walk in one hour in kilometres?

㉚ Ethan's middle finger is 10.6 cm long. His ring finger is 9 mm shorter. How long is his ring finger in centimetres?

E

Copy and complete.

(1) 2.7 km = ☐ m

(2) 1.38 km = ☐ m

(3) 3600 m = ☐ km

(4) 2570 m = ☐ km

(5) 1.4 m = ☐ cm

(6) 3.61 m = ☐ cm

(7) 528 cm = ☐ m

(8) 217 cm = ☐ m

(9) 2.9 cm = ☐ mm

(10) 1.5 cm = ☐ mm

(11) 3 mm = ☐ cm

(12) 98 mm = ☐ cm

Suggest a suitable metric unit to measure these lengths.

(13) a staple

(14) the length of the River Nile

(15) a school corridor

(16) an ear stud

(17) a fork

(18) a plane journey

Copy and complete by putting >, < or = in the box.

(19) 4.9 cm ☐ 490 mm

(20) 720 mm ☐ 0.72 m

(21) 100 m ☐ 0.08 km

(22) 250 m ☐ 0.25 km

(23) 9.9 cm ☐ 0.1 m

(24) 66 cm ☐ 0.166 m

(25) A cyclist travels 2 km in eight minutes. How far in metres does she cycle in one minute?

(26) Jacob jumps 1.95 m. The winning jump is 17 cm higher. What is the height of the winning jump?

(27) A golf hole is 0.43 km long. A golfer drives the ball 264 m. How much further does he have to play?

(28) There are 24 tiles in a stack. Each tile is 8 mm thick. How high is the stack in centimetres?

(29) Each paper tissue is 20 cm long. How many metres of paper are needed to fill a box with 150 tissues?

(30) Seven people take part in a sponsored swim. The table below shows how far they swam.

Ben	1.3 km	Sophie	1.75 km
Colin	1.2 km	Leanne	975 m
Zoe	650 m	Jack	800 m
Matt	725 m		

Mr Harcourt kindly offers to give £2.50 for every 200 m they swam in total. How much money does Mr Harcourt hand over?

On this page you will learn to use the metric measures of capacity, litres and millilitres.

1000 ml = 1 litre	500 ml = 0.500 litres	250 ml = 0.250 litres	100 ml = 0.100 litres
	= 0.5 litres	= 0.25 litres	= 0.1 litres

M

Copy and complete by writing the missing number in the box.

1. 1 litre = ⬜ ml
2. 1.25 litres = ⬜ ml
3. 0.75 litres = ⬜ ml
4. 2.300 litres = ⬜ ml
5. 3000 ml = ⬜ litres
6. 2500 ml = ⬜ litres
7. 250 ml = ⬜ litres
8. 1900 ml = ⬜ litres
9. 3.5 litres = ⬜ ml
10. 0.6 litres = ⬜ ml
11. 400 ml = ⬜ litres
12. 3750 ml = ⬜ litres

Which metric unit would you use to measure the capacity of:

13. a washing machine

14. a jar of peaches
15. an eyebath
16. a paddling pool
17. a can of cola
18. a stream?

E

1. A bottle of lemonade holds one litre. One quarter of it is drunk. How much lemonade is left in the bottle?

2. An ink cartridge holds 15 ml. It can be filled twenty times from an ink bottle. How much ink is in the bottle?

3. Five children share a 2 litre bottle of cola.
How much cola does each child have?

4. 200 ml of water is poured into a bowl. One and a half litres is added. How much water is in the bowl?

5. A shower uses 50 ml of water every second.
How much water does it use in one minute?

6. Hannah pours 0.2 litres of water into a beaker. When she has finished an experiment there is 40 ml of water left. How much water has been used?

Reading Scales

On this page you will learn to read scales accurately.

For each of the scales work out:

a) the measurement indicated by each of the arrows.
b) the difference between the two arrows.

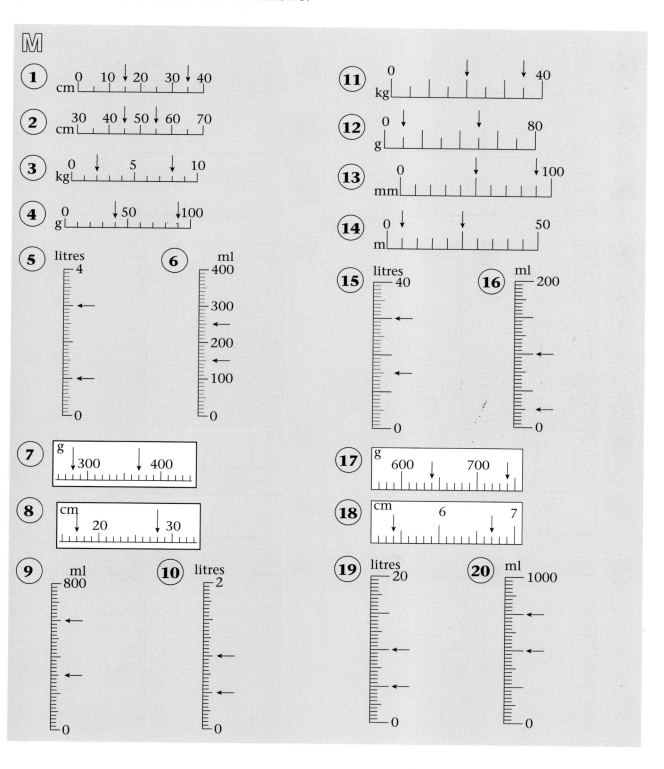

E

For each of the scales work out:

a) the measurement indicated by each of the arrows.

b) the difference between the two arrows.

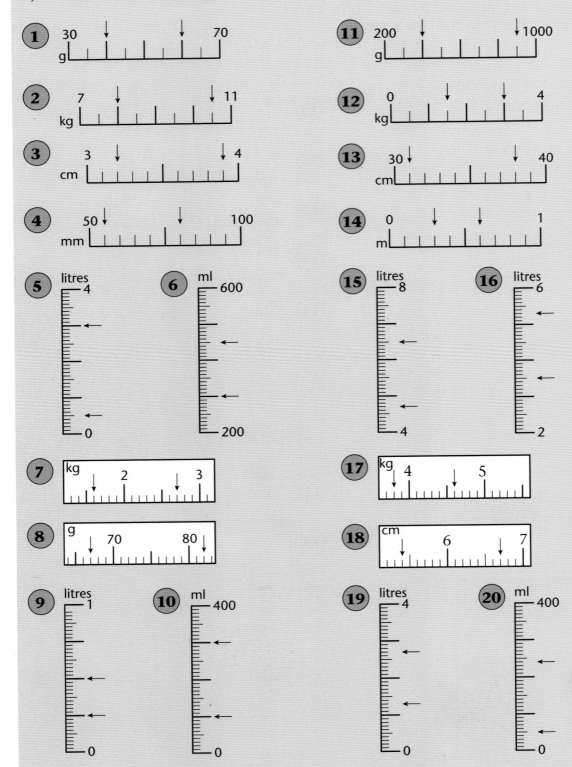

On these pages you will find the perimeter and area of rectangles and shapes made from rectangles.

The area of a shape is the amount of surface it covers.
It is measured in squares, usually square metres (m²) or square centimetres (cm²).

The perimeter of a shape is the distance around its edges.
It is a length and is measured in units of length such as metres or centimetres.

To understand the difference between area and perimeter think of a field.
The perimeter is the fence. The area is the field itself.

Example

6 cm

4 cm

Area = length × width ($l × w$)
= (6 × 4) cm² = 24 cm²
Perimeter = 6 + 4 + 6 + 4
= 20 cm

M

1 Find the perimeter of each rectangle. All lengths are in cm.

a)
7
5   5
7

b)
8
2

c)
6
3

d)
10
6

2 Find the area of each rectangle in Question **1** above.

3 Find the perimeter of each picture.

a)

3 cm

3 cm

b)
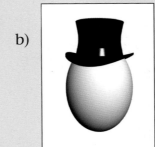
4 cm

3 cm

4 Use squared paper. Draw 3 different rectangles each with a perimeter of 24 cm. Work out the area of each rectangle.

5 Use squared paper. Draw 3 different rectangles each with an area of 24 cm². Work out the perimeter of each rectangle.

6 Find the area of a square where each side is 6 cm.

7 Find the perimeter of a rectangle with a length of 9 cm and a width of 7 cm.

Many shapes are made from rectangles.

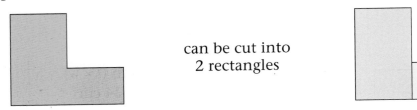

can be cut into 2 rectangles

To find the area of the large shape, find the area of each rectangle then add them together.

Example

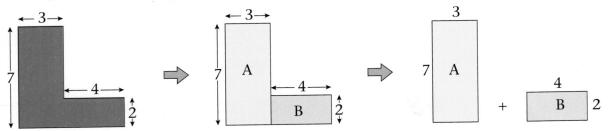

Area rectangle A = 3 × 7 = 21
Area rectangle B = 2 × 4 = 8
Total area = 21 + 8 = 29
If each length is given in cm, the area of the shape is 29 cm².

E

Use rectangles to find the area of each shape in Questions **1** to **8**. All lengths are in cm.

1

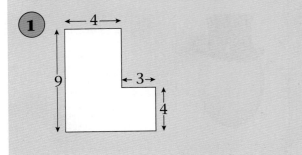

2

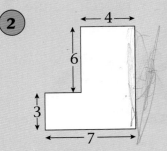

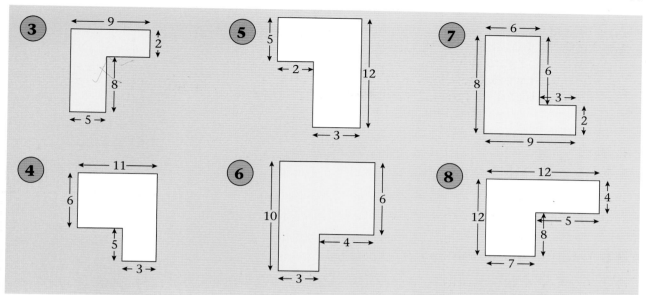

Example

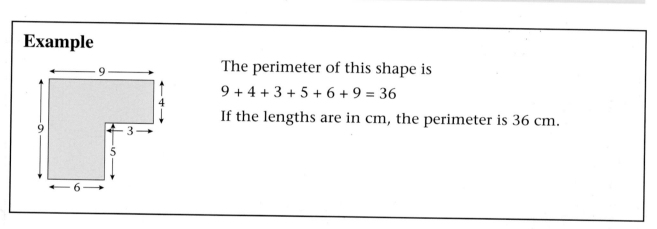

The perimeter of this shape is

9 + 4 + 3 + 5 + 6 + 9 = 36

If the lengths are in cm, the perimeter is 36 cm.

In Questions ⑨ to ⑫, find the perimeter of each shape. All lengths are in cm.

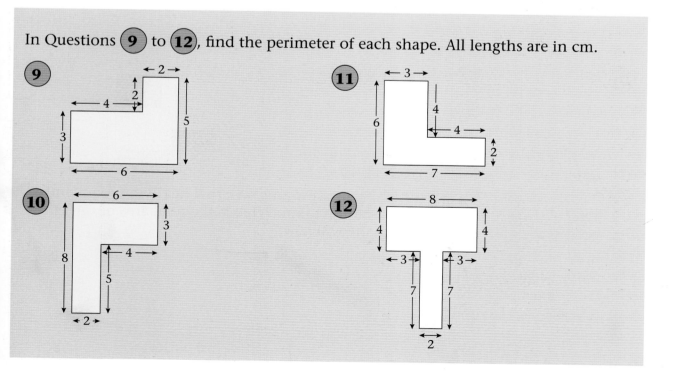

13 Find the perimeter of this shape.
(*Warning*: some sides have no numbers.
You must work these out first.)
All lengths are in cm.

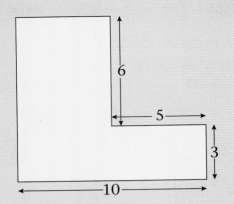

14 Find the area of the shape in Qn. **13**.

15 Find the perimeter of this shape.
(*Warning*: some sides have no numbers.
You must work these out first.)
All lengths are in cm.

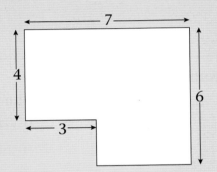

16 Find the area of the shape in Qn. **15**.

17
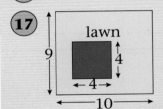

a) Find the area of the lawn. All lengths are in metres.
b) A can of weedkiller covers 10 m² and costs £2. How much
   will it cost to spray the whole lawn with this weedkiller?

18 Repeat question **17** for this new lawn.

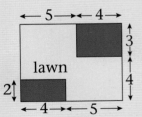

19
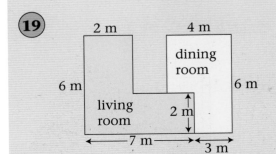

Shannon wants to carpet her living room and
dining room. What is the total area of carpet
she will need?

On these pages you will find the perimeter and area of triangles and shapes made from triangles and rectangles.

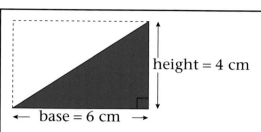

Area of triangle = ½ area of rectangle

$= \frac{1}{2}$ of (6 × 4)

$= \frac{1}{2}$ of 24

= 12 cm²

We say

area of triangle = ½ (base × height)

Example

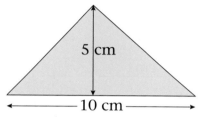

height = 5 cm
base = 10 cm

area of triangle = ½ (base × height)

$= \frac{1}{2}(10 × 5) = \frac{1}{2}(50) = 25$ cm²

Ⓜ

In Questions ① to ⑫, find the area of each triangle.

All lengths are in cm.

①

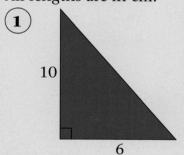

10

6

③

8

4

⑤

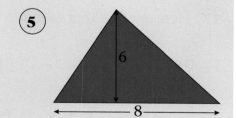

6

8

②

9

5

④

12

3

⑥

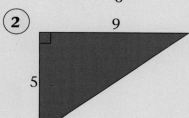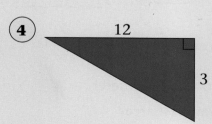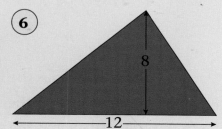

8

12

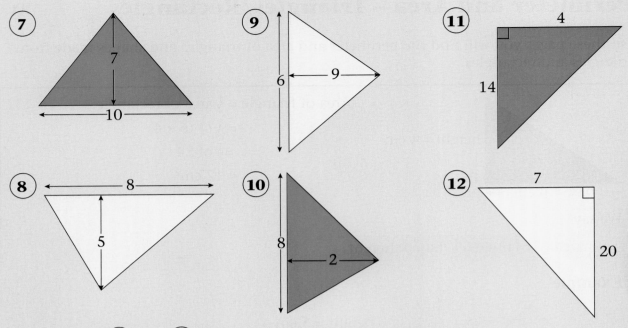

(7) 7, 10

(9) 6, 9

(11) 4, 14

(8) 8, 5

(10) 8, 2

(12) 7, 20

In Questions **(13)** and **(14)**, find the perimeter of each triangle.

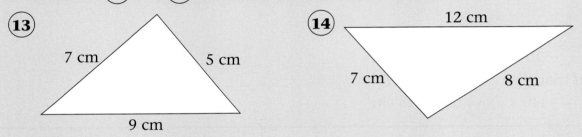

(13) 7 cm, 5 cm, 9 cm

(14) 12 cm, 7 cm, 8 cm

(15) Find the area of a triangle with a base of 12 cm and a height of 7 cm.

(16) Find the area of a triangle with a base of 30 cm and a height of 20 cm.

(17) Here are five shapes made from equilateral triangles of side 1 cm.

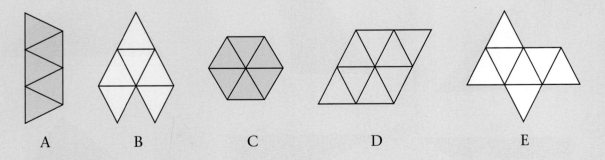

A   B   C   D   E

a) Which shape has the longest perimeter?

b) Which shape has the smallest area?

c) Which shape has the same perimeter as D?

Use triangles and rectangles to find the area of each shape in Questions **1** to **8**.
All lengths are in cm.

1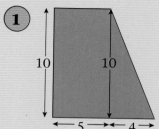

2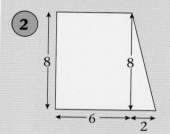

3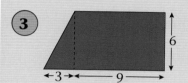

4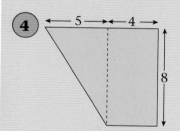

5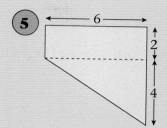

6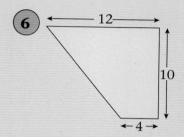

7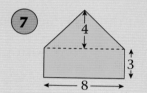

8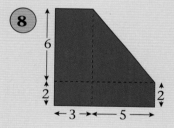

In each of Questions **9** to **12**, find the blue area.
All lengths are in cm.

9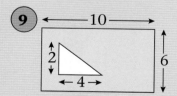

10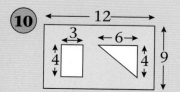

11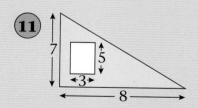

12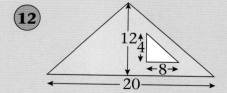

On these pages you will find the surface area of different cuboids.

M

1 Find the area of the front face of the following cuboids:

a)

6 cm
4 cm

c)

6 cm
4 cm
2 cm

b)

5 cm
2 cm
4 cm

d)

2 cm
3 cm
10 cm

2 Write down the area of the back face to each cuboid in Question **1**.

3 Find the total area of the top and bottom faces of the following cuboids:

a)

4 cm
10 cm
6 cm

c)

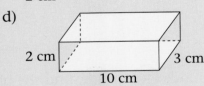

10 cm
4 cm
2 cm

b)

2 cm
3 cm
4 cm

d)

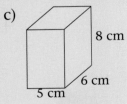

2 cm
3 cm
10 cm

4 Find the total area of the 2 side faces of the following cuboids:

a)

3 cm
10 cm
2 cm

c)

8 cm
6 cm
5 cm

b)

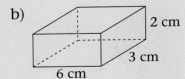

2 cm
3 cm
6 cm

d)

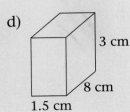

3 cm
8 cm
1.5 cm

5 Copy and complete the tables below to find the total surface area of each cuboid.

a)

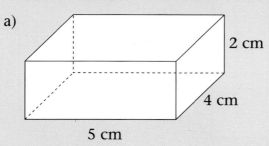

face	Area (cm²)
Front	10
Back	10
Top	20
Bottom	
Side 1	
Side 2	
Total =	

b)

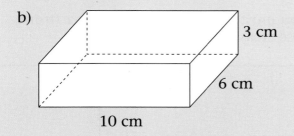

face	Area (cm²)
Front	30
Back	
Top	
Bottom	
Side 1	
Side 2	
Total =	

c)

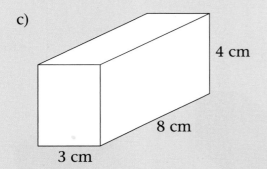

face	Area (cm²)
Front	12
Back	
Top	
Bottom	
Side 1	
Side 2	
Total =	

d)

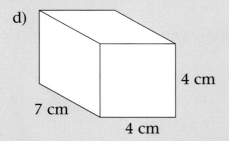

face	Area (cm²)
Front	
Back	
Top	
Bottom	
Side 1	
Side 2	
Total =	

6 Find the *total surface area* of the following cubes:

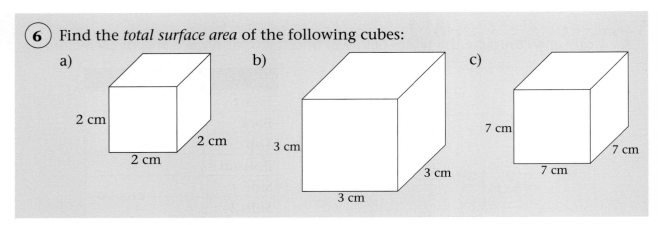

a) 2 cm, 2 cm, 2 cm

b) 3 cm, 3 cm, 3 cm

c) 7 cm, 7 cm, 7 cm

Remember:

To find the *total surface area* of a cuboid, you must find the *area of each face* (front, back, top, bottom and 2 sides) and *add* these areas together.

E

In Questions **1** to **6**, find the *total surface area* of each cuboid:

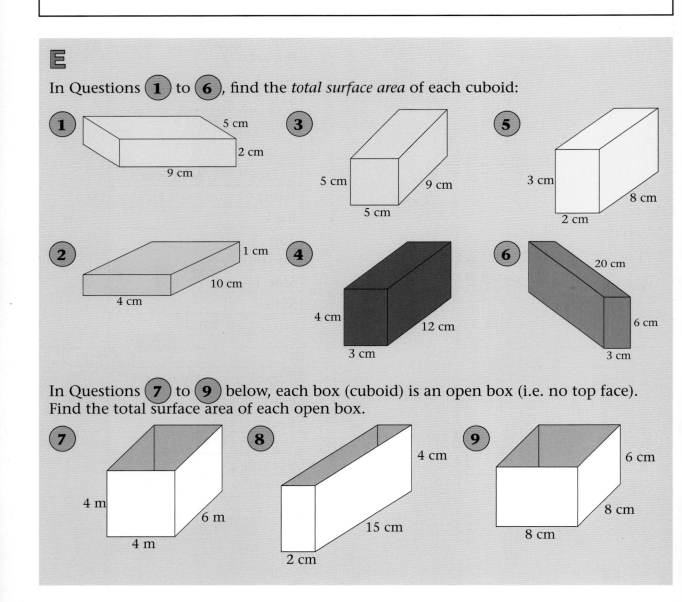

1 5 cm, 2 cm, 9 cm

3 5 cm, 5 cm, 5 cm, 9 cm

5 3 cm, 2 cm, 8 cm

2 1 cm, 10 cm, 4 cm

4 4 cm, 3 cm, 12 cm

6 20 cm, 6 cm, 3 cm

In Questions **7** to **9** below, each box (cuboid) is an open box (i.e. no top face). Find the total surface area of each open box.

7 4 m, 6 m, 4 m

8 2 cm, 15 cm, 4 cm

9 6 cm, 8 cm, 8 cm

Volume of a Cuboid

On these pages you will use a formula to work out the volumes of cuboids.

This cube has a volume of 1 cm³
(1 cubic centimetre)

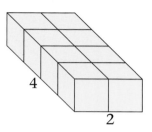

This cuboid has a volume of 8 cm³
(8 cubes, i.e. 4 × 2)

Put 3 layers together like below:

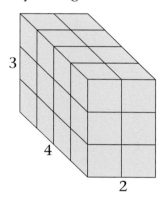

3 layers of 8 cubes gives 3 × 8 = 24 cubes
so volume of cuboid = 24 cm³

So volume of cuboid = 4 × 2 × 3 = 24 cm³.

Volume of a cuboid is given by the formula:

Volume = length × width × height

V = lwh

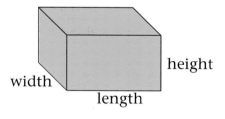

height

width

length

Ⓜ

Find the volume of each cuboid in Questions ① to ⑨ (Answer in cm³).

1

2 cm
2 cm
2 cm

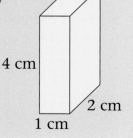
2

4 cm
2 cm
1 cm

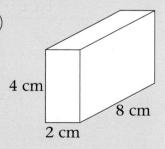
3

4 cm
8 cm
2 cm

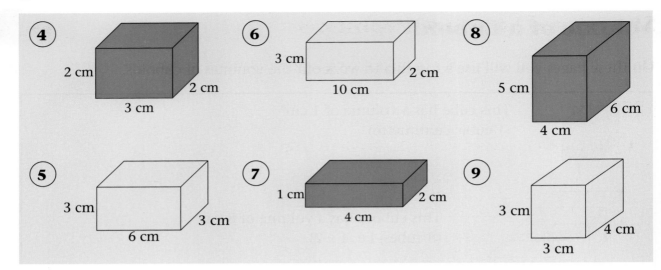

④ 2 cm · 2 cm · 3 cm

⑤ 3 cm · 3 cm · 6 cm

⑥ 3 cm · 2 cm · 10 cm

⑦ 1 cm · 2 cm · 4 cm

⑧ 5 cm · 6 cm · 4 cm

⑨ 3 cm · 4 cm · 3 cm

E

1 (a) Draw a sketch of a 5 cm by 5 cm by 2 cm cuboid.

(b) Work out the volume of this cuboid (Answer in cm^3).

2 (a) Draw a sketch of a 6 cm by 3 cm by 5 cm cuboid.

(b) Work out the volume of this cuboid (Answer in cm^3).

3 Copy and complete the following table.

	Length	Width	Height	Volume
a)	2 cm	4 cm	8 cm	cm^3
b)	3 cm	7 cm	2 cm	cm^3
c)		4 cm	6 cm	72 cm^3
d)	5 cm		4 cm	100 cm^3
e)	9 cm	3 cm		27 cm^3
f)	12.5 cm	2 cm	4 cm	cm^3
g)	8 cm	0.5 cm	10 cm	cm^3

4 Work out the volume of this solid.

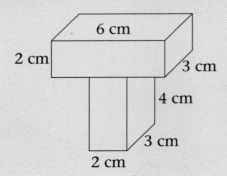

6 cm · 2 cm · 3 cm · 4 cm · 3 cm · 2 cm

Hint: Find the volume of the top cuboid.
Find the volume of the bottom cuboid.
Add the 2 volumes together.

On these pages you will work at a mixture of questions using shapes and measures.

M

1 Here are four shapes made with centimetre squares.

a) Which shape has an area of 5 cm²?

b) Which two shapes have the same perimeter?

2 How many grams of sugar must be added to 1.3 kg to make 3 kg altogether?

3 A builder needs 2 kg of sand. He has 680 g left. How much more sand does he need?

4 Gary is 1.41 m tall. His father is 36 cm taller.

How tall is Gary's father?

5 Which cuboid has the larger volume?

6 A bottle of handwash contains $\frac{1}{2}$ litre.

If 200 ml is used, how much handwash is left?

7 An athlete trains by running 300 m eight times and 200 m six times.

How many kilometres does the athlete run in total?

8 Which shape has the larger area?

9 Use squared paper. Draw 3 different rectangles each with an area of 12 cm².
Work out the perimeter of each rectangle.

10 A birthday card rests on a horizontal table.
Copy these sentences and fill the space with one of the words:

'vertical;   horizontal;   parallel;   perpendicular'

a) The edge BC is _____.

b) The edge AB is _____ to edge AD.

c) Edges DE and DC are _____.

1 Samantha cuts 4 strips of 52 cm from a 3 m length of wood. How long is the wood that is left?

2 One parcel weighs 470 g. A second parcel weights 200 g more. What is the total weight of both parcels in kilograms?

3 Use squared paper.

a) Draw at least four rectangles which have a perimeter of 20 cm.

b) Work out the area of each rectangle.

c) Which of your rectangles has the largest area?

4 How many small boxes will fit into the large box?

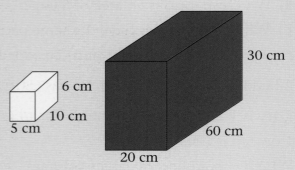

5 A sprinkler uses 60 ml of water every second. How many litres does it use in one minute?

6 A rectangular table has a perimeter of 5 m. It is 68 cm wide. What is its length?

7 Find the area of this shape

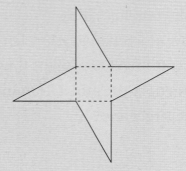

where each triangle is like this:

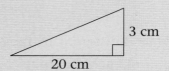

8 Each of the shapes here has an area of 2 cm².

a) On square dotty paper draw three more shapes with area 2 cm²

b) Draw three shapes with area 3 cm².

c) Draw one shape with area 4 cm² and perimeter 10 cm.

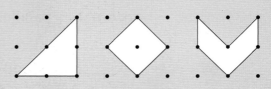

1 Tom and Helen each have 18 sweets.

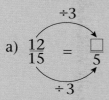

a) Tom eats $\frac{1}{3}$ of his sweets.

How many sweets does Tom eat?

b) Helen eats $\frac{5}{6}$ of her sweets.

How many sweets does Helen eat?

2 Copy and fill in the empty boxes below.

a) $\frac{12}{15} = \frac{\square}{5}$ ($\div 3$)

b) $\frac{18}{24} = \frac{3}{\square}$

3 Write these fractions in order, *starting with the smallest.*

(Remember: make the denominators (bottom numbers) the same *first*)

$\frac{1}{3}$ $\frac{5}{12}$ $\frac{1}{4}$ $\frac{1}{2}$

4 Harpo ate $\frac{2}{5}$ of a cake. Shanta ate $\frac{1}{5}$ of the cake.

What *total fraction* of the cake has been eaten?

5 a) What is the area of this rectangle?

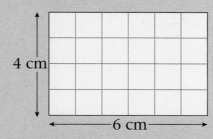

b) The rectangle is used to make 4 triangles. Each triangle is the same size.

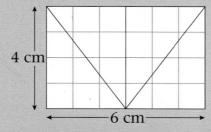

What is the area of *one* of the triangles?

c) The 4 triangles are used to
   make a parallelogram.
   What is the area of the
   parallelogram?

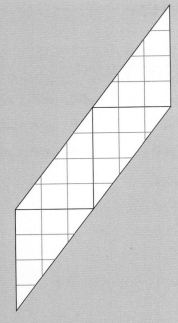

Find the area of this shape.

6

8 cm

3 cm

5 cm

10 cm

7 cm

3 cm

7 Find the area of
this triangle.

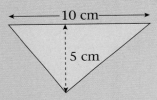

10 cm

5 cm

8 10% of £40 = £4

5% of £40 = £2

so 15% of £40 = £6

Work out

a) 15% of £60   b) 15% of £70

9 *Decrease £80 by 20%.*

10 Write the numbers below as fractions.

a) 0.8   b) 19%   c) 0.321

11

37 × 26 = 962	37 × 27 = 999
37 × 28 = 1036	

Use this table to answer the following questions:

a) 1036 ÷ 28   b) 999 ÷ 37

12 A spinner has *six* equal sections.

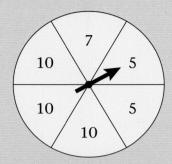

a) What is the probability of scoring 5 on the spinner?

b) What is the probability of scoring a *prime number* on the spinner?

13 I throw a fair coin.

The probability of getting a head is $\frac{1}{2}$.

Is this true? Explain your answer.

14 A security lock has the following buttons.

The code to open the lock is one single digit number followed by one letter.

For example: 2A.

How many *different* codes are there altogether?

Show your working.

15 'The door to my room is 2 km high'.

Is this statement sensible? If not, change this statement so that it *is* sensible.

16 Sam has 2.5 kg of potatoes.

He uses 800 g of potatoes.

What is the total weight of the remaining potatoes?

17 a) What mass do these
    scales show?

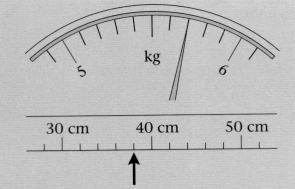

b) What length does this
   arrow point to?

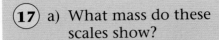

18 The scale opposite shows miles and kilometres.
Use the scale to answer these questions.
a) About how many kilometres is *15 miles*?
b) About how many miles is *20 kilometres*?

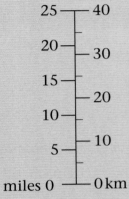

19 These cuboids are made from small cubes.

Write down how many small cubes there are in each cuboid.

a)

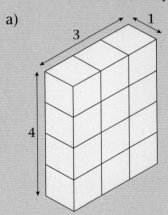

b)

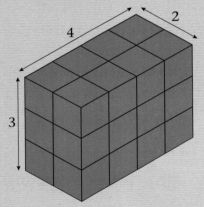

c)

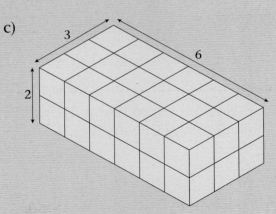

On these pages you will draw shapes in distorted grids.

- Below the word 'Hi' is shown on an ordinary grid and also on a distorted grid.

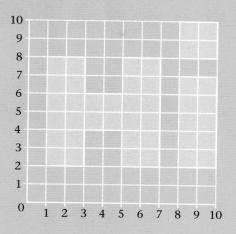

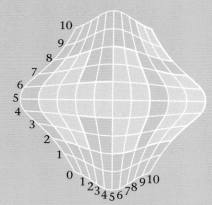

- You can achieve some interesting results by drawing shapes on the grids on the next two pages.

  Ask your teacher for a photo-copy of the grids.

- Begin by drawing some or all of these shapes.

  a) (1, 1) (1, 5) (3, 5) (3, 3) (5, 3) (5, 9) (7, 9) (7, 1) (1, 1).

  b) (1, 5) (1, 7) (5, 7) (5, 9) (7, 9) (7, 7) (9, 7) (9, 5) (7, 5) (7, 1) (5, 1) (5, 5) (1, 5).

  c) (2, 4) (2, 9) (3, 9) (3, 5) (5, 5) (5, 6) (6, 6) (6, 5) (8, 5) (8, 4) (6, 4) (6, 2) (5, 2) (5, 4) (2, 4).

  d) (4, 1) (8, 5) (8, 6) (7, 7) (5, 7) (4, 6) (3, 7) (4, 6) (3, 7) (4, 8) (7, 8) (9, 6) (9, 5) (6, 2) (9, 2) (9, 1) (4, 1).

- Now draw any shape of your own design. It could be the first letter of your names ... or a bird ... or a box. It's up to you. Colour in your designs.

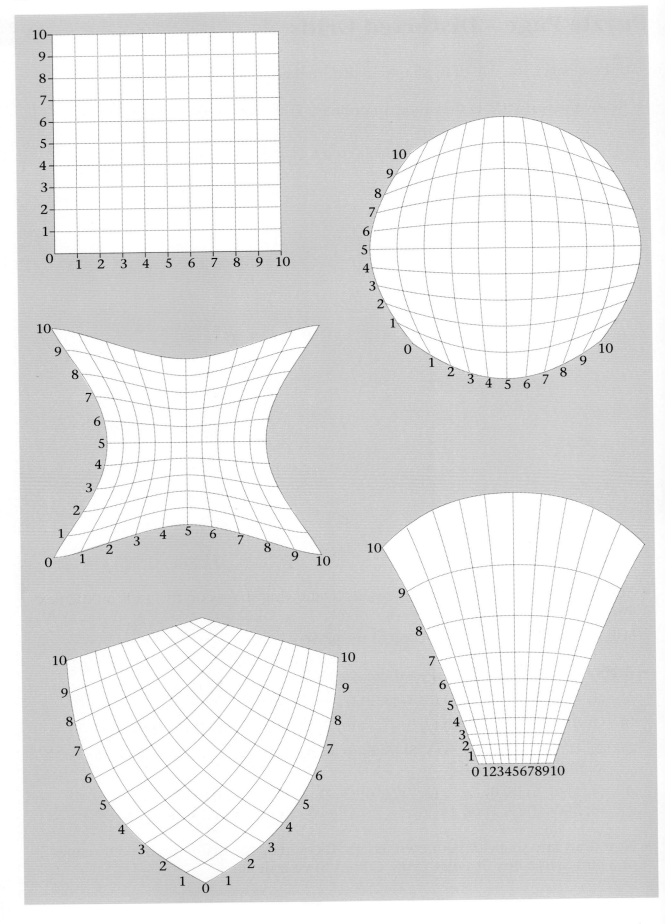

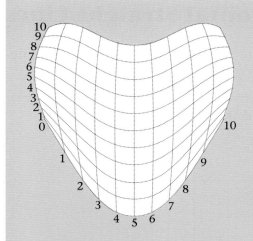

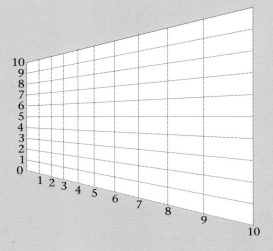

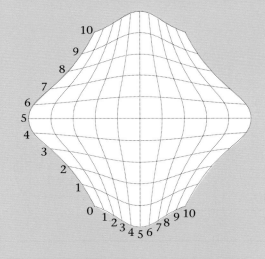

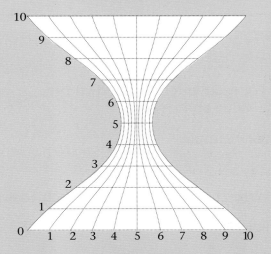

Vertical and Horizontal Straight Lines

On these pages you will learn how to name straight line graphs which are parallel to the *x-axis* or *y-axis*.

On a graph the *vertical* ('going up') axis is often called the *y-axis*.
The *horizontal* ('going across') axis is called the *x-axis*.

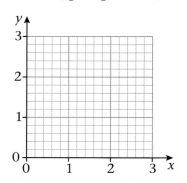
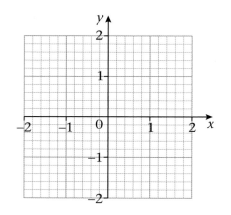

Example

Draw axes and put a cross at the point where $x = 3$ and $y = 1$.

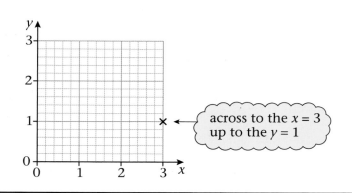

across to the $x = 3$
up to the $y = 1$

This is the point (3, 1)

(3, 1) means $x = 3$, $y = 1$.

---

1 For each letter, write down the x value and y value.

For example:

A is $x = 2$, $y = 3$.

Write the coordinates after each answer.

For example:

A is $x = 2$, $y = 3$ (2, 3)

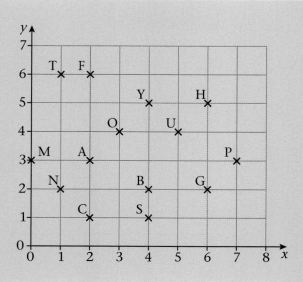

2 Use squared paper.

Copy these axes.

Show each letter below on your grid.

(Letter A is done for you.)

A is $x = 5$, $y = 2$ F is $x = 5$, $y = 5$
B is $x = 3$, $y = 4$ G is $x = 0$, $y = 3$
C is $x = 3$, $y = 6$ H is $x = 2$, $y = 4$
D is $x = 1$, $y = 3$ I is $x = 2$, $y = 1$
E is $x = 6$, $y = 0$ J is $x = 0$, $y = 0$

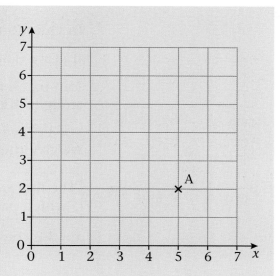

3

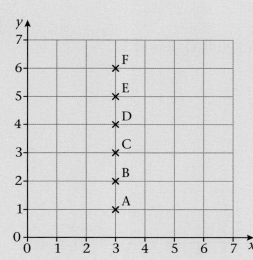

For each letter, write down the x-value and y-value. Write your answer in a table like below.

A	$x = 3$, $y = 1$
B	$x = ...$, $y = ...$
C	
D	
E	
F	

What can you say about the x-value for each letter?

4

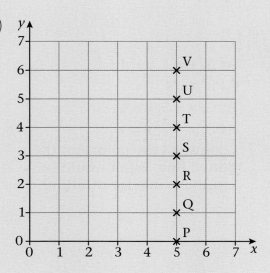

For each letter, write down the x-value and y-value.

What can you say about the x-value for each letter?

In Question ③ earlier we found that $x = 3$ at each letter.

Join up all the crosses with a straight line

$x = 3$ at every place on this line so we give this line the name '$x = 3$'.

> The line $x = 3$ is a vertical line which passes through $x = 3$

$x = 3$ is the *equation* of the line.

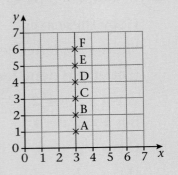

E

① Write down the equation for the lines marked P, Q, R and S.

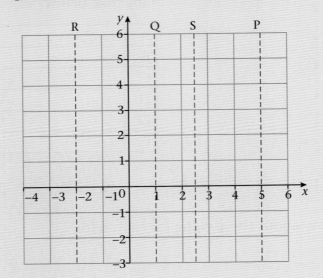

②

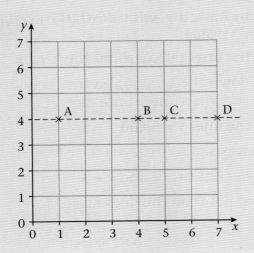

At A, $x = 1$, $y = 4$

At B, $x = 4$, $y = 4$

At C, $x = 5$, $y = 4$

At D, $x = 7$, $y = 4$

Look at all the points on the dotted line. What would be a sensible name for this line?

3 Write down the equations for the lines marked A, B and C.

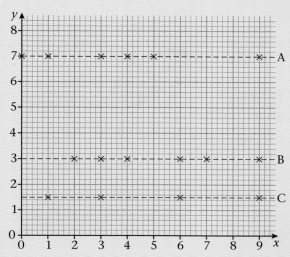

In Questions **4** and **5** there is a line of dots A, a line of crosses B and a line of circles C.

Write down the equations of the lines in each question.

4

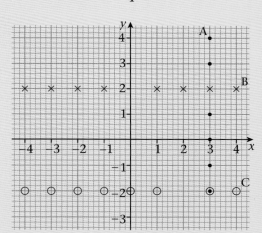

5

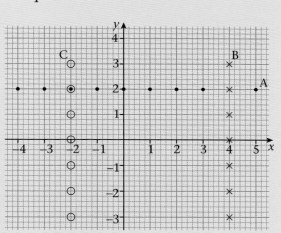

6 On squared paper, draw an x-axis from 0 to 7 and a y-axis from 0 to 7 like below.

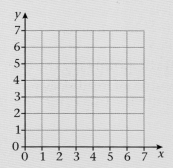

a) Draw the lines $y = 2$ and $x = 3$.

Write down the x-value and the y-value of the point where the 2 lines meet.

b) Draw the lines $y = 5$ and $x = 1$.

At what point do the lines meet?

c) Draw the lines $x = 7$ and $y = 3$.

At what point do the lines meet?

On these pages you will learn how to use formulas to draw straight line graphs.

Example

Use the equation $y = x + 2$ to find 5 coordinates.
Plot these coordinates on a graph.
Join them up to make a straight line graph.

Answer

Pick 5 easy x-values: 0, 1, 2, 3, 4
Use $y = x + 2$ to find y-values which belong with each x-value.
When $x = 0$, $y = x + 2 = 0 + 2 = 2$
  put in equation

so one point is $\boxed{x = 0, \ y = 2 \ (0, 2)}$

When $x = 1$, $y = x + 2 = 1 + 2 = 3$
  put in equation

so one point is $\boxed{x = 1, \ y = 3 \ (1, 3)}$

When $x = 2$, $y = x + 2 = 2 + 2 = 4$
  put in equation

so one point is $\boxed{x = 2, \ y = 4 \ (2, 4)}$

When $x = 3$, $y = x + 2 = 3 + 2 = 5$
  put in equation

so one point is $\boxed{x = 3, \ y = 5 \ (3, 5)}$

When $x = 4$, $y = x + 2 = 4 + 2 = 6$
  put in equation

so one point is $\boxed{x = 4, \ y = 6 \ (4, 6)}$

Draw axes, plot the 5 points and join them up to make a straight line.

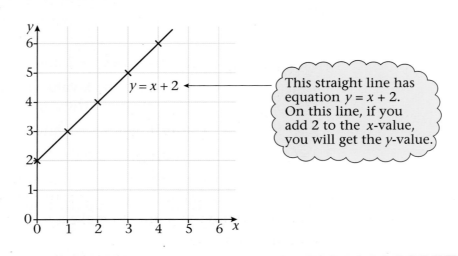

$y = x + 2$

This straight line has equation $y = x + 2$. On this line, if you add 2 to the x-value, you will get the y-value.

1 The equation of a line is $y = x + 3$.

Use x-values: 0, 1, 2, 3, 4

Copy and complete this list of y-values which belong with each x-value.

$x = 0,$	$y = x + 3 = 0 + 3 = 3$	$(0, 3)$
$x = 1,$	$y = x + 3 = 1 + 3 = 4$	$(1, 4)$
$x = 2,$	$y = x + 3 = 2 + 3 = \square$	$(2, \square)$
$x = 3,$	$y = x + 3 = \ldots = \square$	$(3, \square)$
$x = 4,$	$y = x + 3 = \ldots = \square$	$(4, \square)$

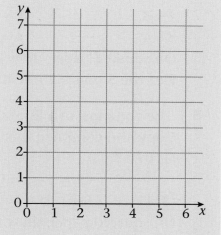

Draw these axes on squared paper.

Plot the 5 points from above.

Join up the points to make a straight line.

The equation of this straight line is $y = x + 3$

2 The equation of a line is $y = x + 5$.

Copy and complete this list of coordinates.

$x = 0,$	$y = x + 5 = 0 + 5 = 5$	$(0, 5)$
$x = 1,$	$y = x + 5 = 1 + 5 = 6$	$(1, 6)$
$x = 2,$	$y = x + 5 = 2 + 5 = \square$	$(2, \square)$
$x = 3,$	$y = x + 5 = \ldots = \square$	$(3, \square)$
$x = 4,$	$y = x + 5 = \ldots = \square$	$(4, \square)$

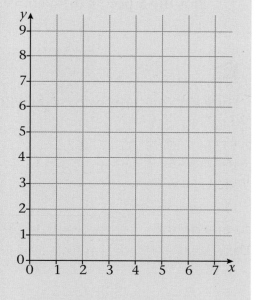

Draw these axes on squared paper.

Plot the 5 points from above.

Join up the points to make a straight line.

The equation of this straight line is $y = x + 5$.

3 The equation of a line is $y = x$.

Copy and complete this list of coordinates.

$x = 0,$ $\qquad$ $y = 0$ $\qquad$ $(0, 0)$

$x = 1,$ $\qquad$ $y = 1$ $\qquad$ $(1, \square)$

$x = 2,$ $\qquad$ $y = \square$ $\qquad$ $(2, \square)$

$x = 3,$ $\qquad$ $y = \square$ $\qquad$ $(3, \square)$

$x = 4,$ $\qquad$ $y = \square$ $\qquad$ $(4, \square)$

On squared paper, draw an x-axis from 0 to 6 and a y-axis from 0 to 6.

Plot the 5 points from above. Join up the points to make a straight line.

The equation of this straight line is $y = x$.

4 The equation of a line is $y = x + 1$.

Copy and complete this list of coordinates.

$x = 0$,	$y = 0 + 1 = 1$	$(0, 1)$
$x = 1$,	$y =$	$(1, \square)$
$x = 2$,	$y =$	$(2, \square)$
$x = 3$,	$y =$	$(3, \square)$
$x = 4$,	$y =$	$(4, \square)$

On squared paper, draw an x-axis from 0 to 6 and a y-axis from 0 to 6.

Plot the 5 points from above. Join up the points to make a straight line.

5 The equation of a line is $y = x - 1$.

Copy and complete this list of coordinates.

$(1, 0)$
$\quad \llcorner y = x - 1 = 1 - 1 = 0.$

$(2, 1) \qquad (3, \square) \qquad (4, \square) \qquad (5, \square)$

On squared paper, draw an x-axis from 0 to 6 and a y-axis from 0 to 6.

Plot the 5 points from above. Join up the points to make a straight line.

E

For each Question below you will need to draw axes like these:

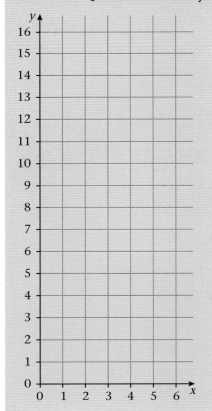

1 $y = 5 - x$

Complete the coordinates:

$(0, 5) \quad (1, 4) \quad (2, \square) \quad (3, \square) \quad (4, \square)$

Plot these points and draw the graph.

2 $y = x - 2$

Complete the coordinates.

$(2, 0) \quad (3, 1) \quad (4, \square) \quad (5, \square) \quad (6, \square)$

Plot these points and draw the graph.

3 $y = 4x$

Complete the coordinates.

$(0, 0) \quad (1, 4) \quad (2, \square) \quad (3, \square) \quad (4, \square)$

Plot these points and draw the graph.

4 $y = 2x + 1$

Complete the coordinates.

$(0, 1) \quad (1, 3) \quad (2, \square) \quad (3, \square) \quad (4, \square)$

Draw the graph.

On these pages you will read from graphs and draw graphs from real-life events.

1 In June 2009, the pound (£) was worth the same as 1.4 Euros (€).
This graph converts pounds into Euros.

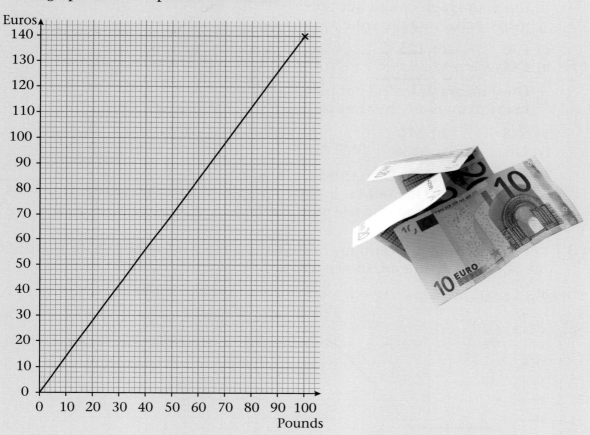

a) What does one little square on the 'Pounds' axis show you?

b) What does one little square on the 'Euros' axis show you?

Use your graph to find out how many Euros are the same as

c) £50   d) £25   e) £75   f) £30

Use your graph to find out how many pounds are the same as

g) €28   h) €98   i) €56   j) €112

2 In June 2009, the pound (£) was worth 1.6 U.S. Dollars ($).

This graph converts pounds into dollars.

a) What does one little square on the 'Pounds' axis show you?

b) What does one little square on the 'Dollars' axis show you?

Use your graph to find out how many dollars are the same as

c) £50   d) £25
e) £35   f) £60

Use your graph to find out how many pounds are the same as

g) $48   h) $70
i) $16   j) $136

k) On holiday in the USA, Chad bought a meal for $40. How many pounds did the meal cost?

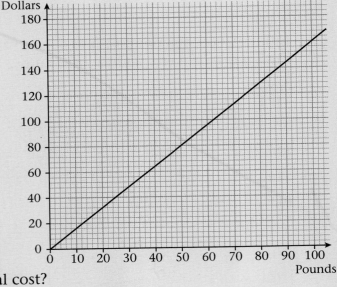

3 The temperature in a centrally heated house is recorded every hour from 12.00 till 24.00; the results are shown below.

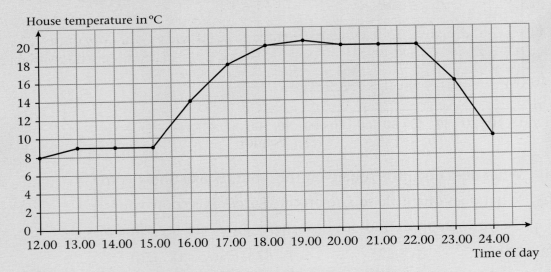

a) What does one square on the time axis show you?

b) What was the temperature at 20.00?

c) Estimate the temperature at 16.30.

d) Estimate the two times when the temperature was 18°C.

e) When do you think the central heating was switched on?

f) When do you think the central heating was switched off?

4 A man climbing a mountain measures his height above sea level after every 30 minutes; the results are shown below.

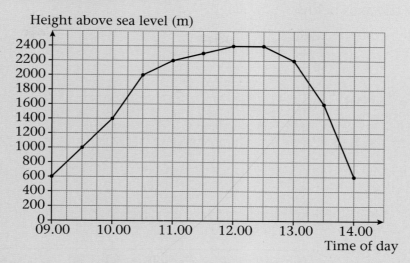

a) What does one square on the time axis show you? Check with your teacher.
b) At what height was he at 10.00?
c) At what height was he at 13.30?
d) Estimate his height above sea level at 09.45.
e) At what two times was he 2200 m above sea level?
f) How high was the mountain? (He got to the top!)
g) How long did he rest at the summit?
h) How long did he take to reach the summit?

5 A car went on a five hour journey starting at 12.00 with a full tank of petrol. The volume of petrol in the tank was measured after every hour; the results are shown below.

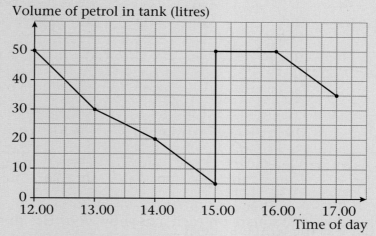

a) How much petrol was in the tank at 13.00?
b) At what time was there 5 litres in the tank?
c) How much petrol was used in the first hour of the journey?
d) What happened at 15.00?
e) What do you think happened between 15.00 and 16.00?
f) How much petrol was used between 12.00 and 17.00?

E

1 Draw the axes below:

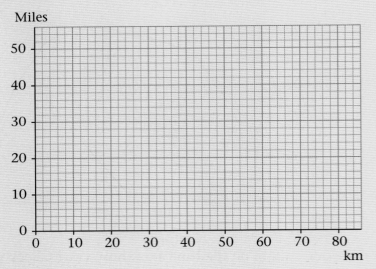

We will draw a graph to convert *kilometres into miles*.

80 km is the same as 50 miles.

Put a 'X' at the point where km = 80 and miles = 50.

Join this point to the point where km = 0 and miles = 0 as shown below (*use a ruler* for a straight line).

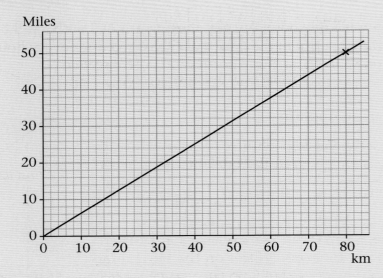

a) What does one square on each axis show you? Use this graph to convert:

b) 40 km into miles.

c) 15 miles into km.

d) 45 miles into km.

e) 64 km into miles.

2 Draw the axes below:

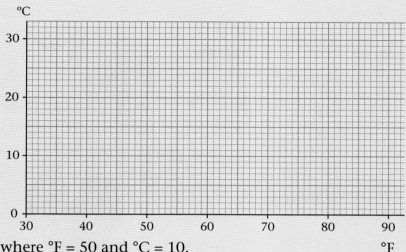

Draw a 'X' where °F = 50 and °C = 10.

Draw another 'X' where °F = 86 and °C = 30.

Use a ruler to draw a long straight line through these 2 points.

This graph can be used to convert temperatures from °F to °C.

Use the graph to convert:

a) 77°F into °C.   b) 15°C into °F.

3 A mobile phone company charges £10 a month rental plus 20p per minute for calls. Some costs are given in the table below:

minutes of calls	0	20	40	60	80
cost in £		10	14	18	22	26

Draw a graph to show this information. Use a scale of 1 cm for every 10 minutes on the horizontal axis and 1 cm for every £5 on the vertical axis. It should look like the graph opposite:

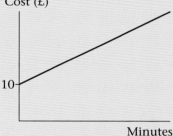

4 Petrol is selling at 80p per litre.

Some costs are given in the table below:

Petrol (litres)	5	10	15	20	25
Cost (£)	4	8	12	16	20

Draw a graph to show this information. Use a scale of 1 cm for every 5 litres on the horizontal axis and 1 cm for every £5 on the vertical axis.

It should look like this:

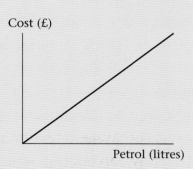

Use your graph to find how much money you pay for

a) 7.5 litres   b) 22.5 litres   c) 12.5 litres

How many litres of petrol will you get for

d) £14   e) £2   f) £3.20?

On these pages you will learn what each digit in a decimal fraction represents.

Examples

three tenths

$\frac{3}{10}$ = 0.3

fifty-seven hundredths

$\frac{57}{100}$ = 0.57

The value of a digit depends upon its position in a number.

Each digit in a number is 10 times higher than the digit to the right. This applies to decimal fractions as well as to whole numbers.

$$\text{T U} \cdot \tfrac{1}{10} \ \ \tfrac{1}{100} \ \ \tfrac{1}{1000}$$

$$30 = 3\ 0 \cdot 0$$
$$3 = \quad 3 \cdot 0$$
$$\tfrac{3}{10} = \quad 0 \cdot 3$$
$$\tfrac{3}{100} = \quad 0 \cdot 0 \ 3$$
$$\tfrac{3}{1000} = \quad 0 \cdot 0 \ \ 0 \ \ 3$$

$$\text{T U} \cdot \tfrac{1}{10} \ \ \tfrac{1}{100} \ \ \tfrac{1}{1000}$$

$$24 = 2\ 4 \cdot 0$$
$$2\tfrac{4}{10} = \quad 2 \cdot 4$$
$$\tfrac{24}{100} = \quad 0 \cdot 2 \ 4$$
$$\tfrac{24}{1000} = \quad 0 \cdot 0 \ 2 \ 4$$

Ⓜ Part 1

What part of each shape is shaded? Write your answer as a fraction and as a decimal fraction.

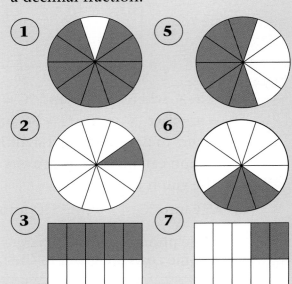

1 **5** **2** **6** **3** **7** **4** **8**

9 Write each number shown by the arrows as a decimal fraction.

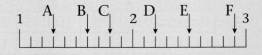

Write each of these numbers as a decimal fraction.

10 $\frac{4}{10}$ **13** $2\frac{9}{10}$ **16** $10\frac{5}{10}$

11 $1\frac{7}{10}$ **14** $6\frac{8}{10}$ **17** $17\frac{2}{10}$

12 $3\frac{3}{10}$ **15** $\frac{6}{10}$ **18** $4\frac{1}{10}$

Part 2

Express the shaded part of each diagram as a fraction and as a decimal fraction.

(1)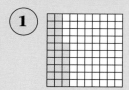

(3)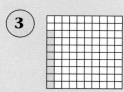

(2)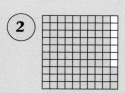

(4)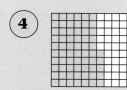

Write each number shown by the arrows as a decimal fraction.

(5)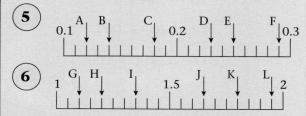

(6)

Give the value of the underlined figure in each of these numbers.

(7) 2.5_8_

(8) 1_8_.67

(9) _4_5.76

(10) 1_6_.53

(11) 13.3_2_

(12) 36._9_

(13) 20._1_3

(14) 7.9_2_

(15) 12._4_1

(16) 2.8_5_

(17) 1.6_1_

(18) 13._2_4

Give the next five terms in each of these sequences.

(19) 0.01, 0.02, 0.03, 0.04, 0.05

(20) 1.0, 1.02, 1.04, 1.06, 1.08

(21) 1.92, 1.93, 1.94, 1.95, 1.96

(22) 0.91, 0.93, 0.95, 0.97, 0.99

(23) 0.6, 0.65, 0.7, 0.75, 0.8

(24) 4.07, 4.06, 4.05, 4.04, 4.03

E

Example

$4 + \frac{6}{10} + \frac{3}{100} + \frac{5}{1000}$

4.635

Write the decimal fraction shown on each abacus.

(1)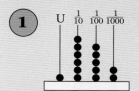

(4)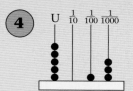

(2)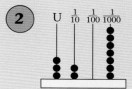

(5)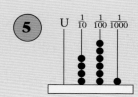

(3)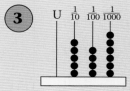

(6)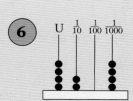

Write these numbers as decimal fractions.

(7) $\frac{3}{100}$

(8) $\frac{263}{1000}$

(9) $1\frac{18}{100}$

(10) $5\frac{169}{1000}$

(11) $\frac{72}{1000}$

(12) $\frac{451}{1000}$

(13) $2\frac{96}{1000}$

(14) $\frac{1}{1000}$

(15) $1\frac{316}{1000}$

(16) $6\frac{9}{100}$

(17) $1\frac{48}{1000}$

(18) $4\frac{5}{1000}$

Give the value of the underlined figure in each of these numbers.

(19) 4._6_2

(20) 16._7_91

(21) 18.13_5_

(22) _6_.472

(23) 11._1_09

(24) 33.3_3_

(25) 41.61_8_

(26) 1_9_.72

(27) 3.0_6_5

(28) 8.54_5_

(29) 0.01_6_

(30) 43.78_9_

On these pages you will learn to multiply and divide whole numbers by 10 and 100.

Examples

×10	digits move 1 place to the left	624 × 10 = 6240
×100	digits move 2 places to the left	624 × 100 = 62 400
÷10	digits move 1 place to the right	4300 ÷ 10 = 430
÷100	digits move 2 places to the right	4300 ÷ 100 = 43

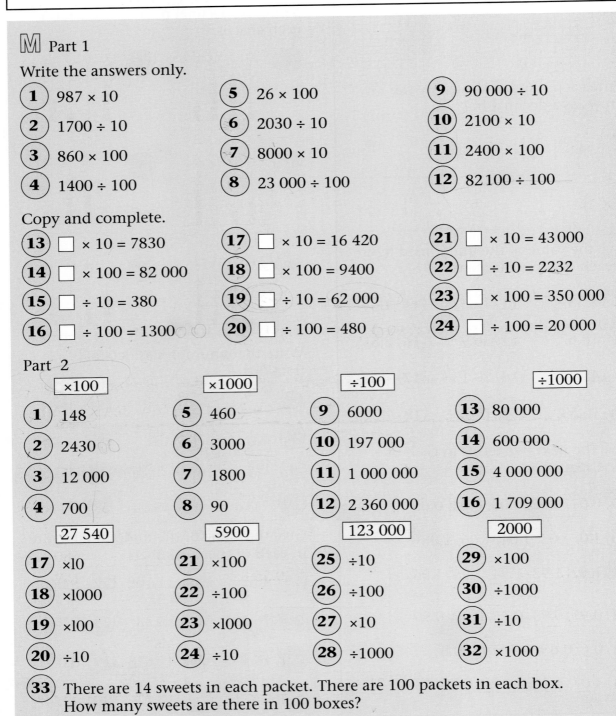

Ⓜ Part 1

Write the answers only.

(1) 987 × 10

(2) 1700 ÷ 10

(3) 860 × 100

(4) 1400 ÷ 100

(5) 26 × 100

(6) 2030 ÷ 10

(7) 8000 × 10

(8) 23 000 ÷ 100

(9) 90 000 ÷ 10

(10) 2100 × 10

(11) 2400 × 100

(12) 82 100 ÷ 100

Copy and complete.

(13) ☐ × 10 = 7830

(14) ☐ × 100 = 82 000

(15) ☐ ÷ 10 = 380

(16) ☐ ÷ 100 = 1300

(17) ☐ × 10 = 16 420

(18) ☐ × 100 = 9400

(19) ☐ ÷ 10 = 62 000

(20) ☐ ÷ 100 = 480

(21) ☐ × 10 = 43 000

(22) ☐ ÷ 10 = 2232

(23) ☐ × 100 = 350 000

(24) ☐ ÷ 100 = 20 000

Part 2

×100	×1000	÷100	÷1000
(1) 148	**(5)** 460	**(9)** 6000	**(13)** 80 000
(2) 2430	**(6)** 3000	**(10)** 197 000	**(14)** 600 000
(3) 12 000	**(7)** 1800	**(11)** 1 000 000	**(15)** 4 000 000
(4) 700	**(8)** 90	**(12)** 2 360 000	**(16)** 1 709 000

27 540	5900	123 000	2000
(17) ×10	**(21)** ×100	**(25)** ÷10	**(29)** ×100
(18) ×1000	**(22)** ÷100	**(26)** ÷100	**(30)** ÷1000
(19) ×100	**(23)** ×1000	**(27)** ×10	**(31)** ÷10
(20) ÷10	**(24)** ÷10	**(28)** ÷1000	**(32)** ×1000

(33) There are 14 sweets in each packet. There are 100 packets in each box. How many sweets are there in 100 boxes?

E

Examples	2.36 × 10 = 23.6	48 ÷ 10 = 4.8
	2.36 × 100 = 236	48 ÷ 100 = 0.48
	3.2 × 10 = 32	5 ÷ 10 = 0.5
	3.2 × 100 = 320	5 ÷ 100 = 0.05

Work out

1 2.7 × 10 . . . .   **5** 44.5 × 10 . . . .   **9** 4 ÷ 10 . . . .

2 3.1 × 100 . . . .   **6** 0.69 × 100 . . . .   **10** 28 ÷ 100 . . . .

3 1.38 × 10 . . . .   **7** 12 ÷ 10 . . . .   **11** 73 ÷ 10 . . . .

4 1.72 × 100 . . . .   **8** 7 ÷ 100 . . . .   **12** 6 ÷ 100 . . . .

Complete by writing the missing numbers.

13 3.5 × ☐ = 35   **19** 6 ÷ ☐ = 0.6

14 ☐ × 100 = 96   **20** ☐ ÷ 100 = 0.35

15 14 ÷ ☐ = 0.14   **21** 1.88 × ☐ = 18.8

16 ☐ ÷ 10 = 4.8   **22** ☐ × 100 = 615

17 5.1 × ☐ = 510   **23** 2 ÷ ☐ = 0.02

18 ☐ × 10 = 263   **24** ☐ ÷ 10 = 3.9

25 A ship sails 8.1 km in one hour. How far does it go in 100 hours?

Complete each table.

26

×10		
0.5	→	5
0.47	→	
	→	9.3
2.6	→	
	→	8
0.09	→	
	→	0.1

27

÷10		
1.8	→	0.18
	→	0.55
22	→	
	→	7.9
0.3	→	
	→	0.3
21.4	→	

28

×100		
6.8	→	680
	→	159
0.25	→	
	→	34
0.03	→	
	→	70
4.5	→	

On this page you will learn to round numbers to the nearest 10,100 or 1000 or the nearest whole number.

Always look at the column to the right of that to which you are rounding.
If the number in that column is less than 5, round down.
If the number in that column is 5 or greater than 5, round up.

Examples

to the nearest 10	362 $\xrightarrow{\text{rounds to}}$ 360	2137 $\xrightarrow{\text{rounds to}}$ 2140
to the nearest 100	5941 $\longrightarrow$ 5900	8681 $\longrightarrow$ 8700
to the nearest 1000	6456 $\longrightarrow$ 6000	7568 $\longrightarrow$ 8000

- To round a decimal fraction to the nearest whole number look at the tenths column.

Examples

To the nearest whole number,   3.5 rounds to 4   5.49 rounds to 5

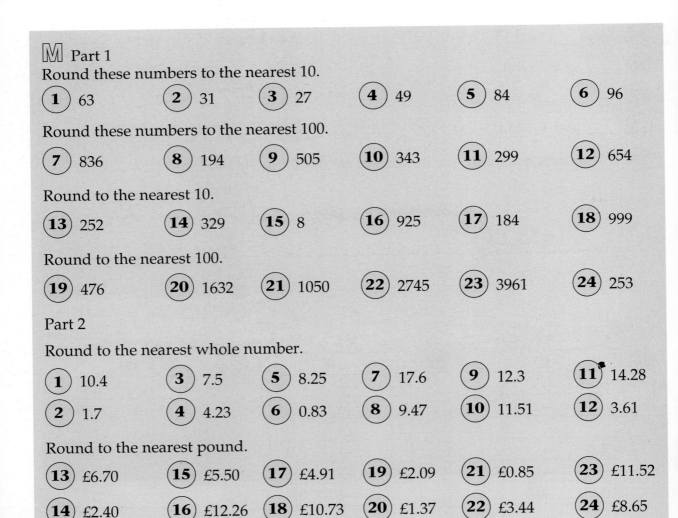

M Part 1

Round these numbers to the nearest 10.

(1) 63   (2) 31   (3) 27   (4) 49   (5) 84   (6) 96

Round these numbers to the nearest 100.

(7) 836   (8) 194   (9) 505   (10) 343   (11) 299   (12) 654

Round to the nearest 10.

(13) 252   (14) 329   (15) 8   (16) 925   (17) 184   (18) 999

Round to the nearest 100.

(19) 476   (20) 1632   (21) 1050   (22) 2745   (23) 3961   (24) 253

Part 2

Round to the nearest whole number.

(1) 10.4   (3) 7.5   (5) 8.25   (7) 17.6   (9) 12.3   (11) 14.28

(2) 1.7   (4) 4.23   (6) 0.83   (8) 9.47   (10) 11.51   (12) 3.61

Round to the nearest pound.

(13) £6.70   (15) £5.50   (17) £4.91   (19) £2.09   (21) £0.85   (23) £11.52

(14) £2.40   (16) £12.26   (18) £10.73   (20) £1.37   (22) £3.44   (24) £8.65

Approximate calculations by rounding to the nearest 10.

Examples

a) $327 + 244 \rightarrow 330 + 240 \rightarrow 570$

b) $42 \times 9 \rightarrow 40 \times 9 \rightarrow 360$

c) $319 - 108 \rightarrow 320 - 110 \rightarrow 210$

d) $22 \times 19 \rightarrow 20 \times 20 \rightarrow 400$

E

Round to the nearest 1000.

1) 6700

2) 11 480

3) 15 620

4) 13 367

5) 7812

6) 9501

Approximate by rounding to the nearest 10.

7) 166 + 122

8) 346 + 533

9) 257 + 142

10) 97 − 29

11) 142 − 53

12) 216 − 78

13) 38 × 5

14) 72 × 6

15) 49 × 8

16) 96 × 7

Copy the sentences, rounding the number to the nearest 1000.

17) Lake Victoria has an area of 69 484 km².

18) The Polar diameter of the Earth is 12 714 km.

19) The car has a mileage of 73 521.

20) Jasmine won £2 319 278 on the Lottery.

Approximate by rounding to the nearest 10.

21) 267 + 142

22) 272 − 64

23) 62 × 7

24) 683 + 279

25) 498 − 317

26) 78 × 9

27) 435 + 183

28) 39 × 8

Round to the nearest:

$\boxed{1}$

29) 16.48

30) 8.943

31) 17.37

32) 4.539

33) 13.75

Round to the nearest:

$\boxed{£1}$

34) £2.67

35) £0.26

36) £7.53

37) £3.85

38) £1.04

Round to the nearest:

$\boxed{1m}$

39) 8.60 m

40) 2.28 m

41) 5.47 m

42) 0.93 m

43) 7.52 m

On this page you will learn to make and justify estimates.

M

Estimate the numbers shown by the arrows.

(1)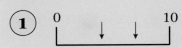

(2)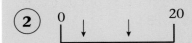

(3)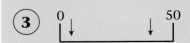

(4)

(5)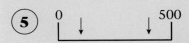

(6) 0 ↓ ↓ 5

(7) Which snake is:

a) half as long as Sally?

b) twice as long as Sylvia?

c) one and a half times the length of Cecil?

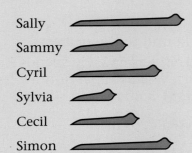

Sally

Sammy

Cyril

Sylvia

Cecil

Simon

(8) Sally is one metre long. Estimate the lengths of the other snakes.

E

(1) Six friends bought drinks. Five minutes later their drinks looked like this.

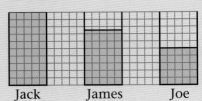

Jack   James   Joe

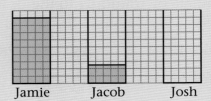

Jamie   Jacob   Josh

Who has drunk:

a) three times as much as James?

b) half as much as Joe?

c) one tenth as much as Josh?

(2) Jack has not touched his drink. Josh has finished his. Estimate the fraction left in the other four glasses.

(3) Estimate how many sheets of A4 paper would be needed to cover:

a) your table.

b) the classroom door.

c) the classroom floor.

1 Find the missing number below:

$$4619 = \boxed{} + 53$$

2 Tariq spent £4.61 on his lunch, £1.60 on a magazine and £2.75 on the bus.

a) How much did Tariq spend in total?

b) How much money would he have left from £10?

3 A bar of chocolate costs 65p.
Find the cost of 32 bars of chocolate.

4 A ticket for a paintball game costs £23.
Jan has £300.

She wants to buy as many tickets as possible.
How many tickets can Jan buy?

5 Work out

$$3.6 \times 7$$

6 Look at the numbers below. Write down the largest number.

$$\boxed{0.023} \qquad \boxed{0.1} \qquad \boxed{0.04}$$

7 If you start with n, multiply by 3 then add 4, you get $3n + 4$.
What do you get if you start with n, multiply by 7 then subtract 5?

8

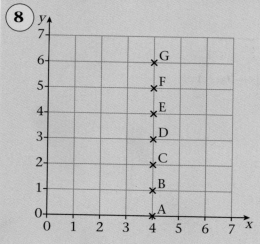

For each letter, write down the x-value and the y-value.

What can you say about the x-value for each letter?

9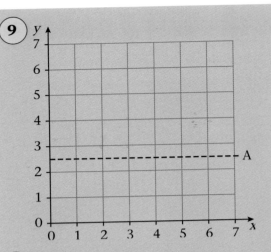

Write down the equation of the dotted line A.

10 Work out

a) 17×100

b) 1.7×100

c) 0.17×100

11

| 2 | 8 | 1 | 4 |

Use some of the four number cards to make numbers that are *as close as possible* to the numbers written below.

Example

50 ⟶ | 4 | 8 |

You must not use the same card more than once in each answer.

a) 30 ⟶ ☐☐

b) 400 ⟶ ☐☐☐

c) 8000 ⟶ ☐☐☐☐

12 Round off the decimals below to the *nearest whole number*.

a) 1.7

b) 3.2

c) 7.62

13 A calculator costs £4.99.
Roughly how much will 11 calculators cost?
(Your answer has to be close but *not exact*)

14 Write the decimals below in order, *starting with the smallest.*

0.6   0.61   0.06   0.5

15 Write the decimals below, *starting with the largest.*

1.08   1.8   1.83   1.18

16 Write the numbers below as decimals.

a) $\frac{4}{10}$ b) 21%   c) $\frac{11}{100}$

17 The equation of a line is $y = x + 2$.

Copy and complete this list of coordinates.

$x = 0, y = 0 + 2 = 2$ (0, 2)

(1, ☐)

(2, ☐)

(3, ☐)

(4, ☐)

On squared paper, draw an x-axis from 0 to 6 and a y-axis from 0 to 6.
Plot the 5 points from above. Join up the points to make a straight line.

18 *Use a calculator* to work out

$$\sqrt{0.09} \times 10$$

19 *Use a calculator* to work out

$$(30 \times 60) + (3 \times 208)$$

20 Tobias and Linford ran an 800 metres race.
The distance-time graph shows the race.

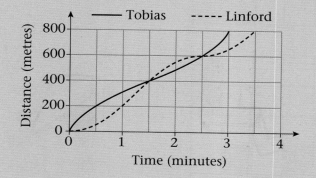

Use the graph to copy and complete the sentences below.

'At 400 metres, Tobias and Linford were level (after .... minutes).

Linford was then in the lead for .... minute.

At .... metres, Tobias and Linford were level again.

.... won the race.'

Here are cross number puzzles with a difference. There are no clues, only answers, and you have to find where the answers go.

a) Copy out the cross number pattern.

b) Fit all the given numbers into the correct spaces. Work logically and tick off the numbers from lists as you write them in the squares.

1

2 digits	3 digits	4 digits	5 digits
23	146	2708	25404
26	235	2715	25814
42	245		37586
57	337		
59	539		
87	695		

2

2 digits	3 digits	4 digits	5 digits
18	244	2163	36918
21	247	4133	46514
31	248	4213	54374
33	332	4215	54704
47	333	4283	87234
63	334	4317	
64	608	4394	
77			

3

2 digits	3 digits	4 digits	5 digits	7 digits
36	145	2286	16145	4235824
52	185	5235	66145	
56	245	5248	66152	
63	246	5249	66272	
65	374	5452	91671	
77	437	6241		
90	646			
	896			

4

2 digits	3 digits	4 digits	5 digits
14	123	1325	14251
22	231	1478	29163
26	341	1687	29613
43	439	1976	29872
65	531	2523	34182
70	670	4798	54875
81		5601	63712
82		5611	67358
		5621	82146
		6109	84359
		8171	97273

6 digits	7 digits
145026	9354234
740136	
983514	

5 This one is more difficult.

2 digits	3 digits	4 digits	5 digits
15	137	2513	29666
19	206	3048	31873
21	276	3214	40657
22	546	3244	43104
28	592	3437	43158
31	783	3514	54732
77		3517	60783
90		3544	62114
		4122	80751
		4127	82614
		6934	93654

6 digits	7 digits
235785	9733764
235815	
452705	

On this page you will learn to sketch the reflection of a shape in a mirror line.

Examples

(1)

(2)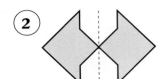

(3)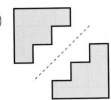

(4) Shade in squares to complete the symmetrical patterns.

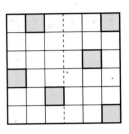 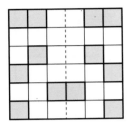

(5) Shade in squares to complete the symmetrical patterns.

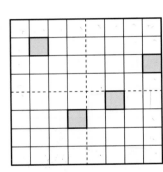 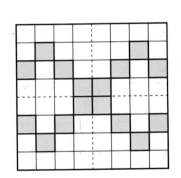

In each of the problems copy the shape and the mirror line and sketch the refléction.

M

(1)

(2)

(3)

(4)

Copy the patterns below on squared paper.
Shade in as many squares as necessary to complete the symmetrical patterns.

(5)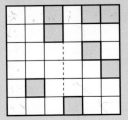

(6)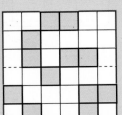

(7)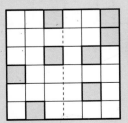

Copy the shape and the mirror line and draw the reflection.

 1

3

5

2

4

6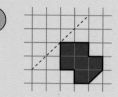

Copy the patterns below on squared paper.
Shade in as many squares as necessary to complete the symmetrical patterns.

7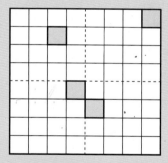

9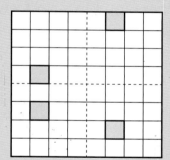

11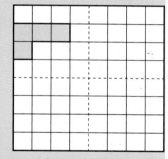

8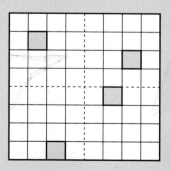

10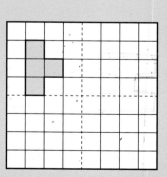

12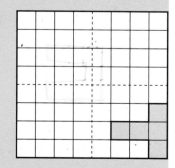

On this page you will learn to sketch the position of a shape after a rotation.

Example

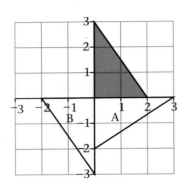

A: 90° rotation
about (0, 0)

B: 180° rotation
about (0, 0)

USEFUL TIPS

(1) Imagine holding the point of rotation down with a pencil point.

(2) 90° rotation – horizontal lines become vertical and vice versa.

(3) 180° rotation – horizontal and vertical remain unchanged.

(4) Use tracing paper.

Ⓜ

Use squared paper. You can use tracing paper. For each of the following shapes:

a) copy the shape.
b) rotate the shape 90° about point A in a clockwise direction.
c) rotate the shape 180° about point A.

(1)   (2)   (3)   (4)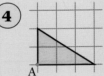

Ⓔ

Copy the following shapes on grids showing all four quadrants, as in the example above. Rotate each shape both 90° and 180° about the origin, (0, 0), in a clockwise direction.

(1)   (2)   (3) 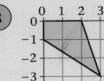 (4)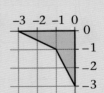

Join up the following points in the order given on grids showing all four quadrants, as in the example above. Rotate each shape about the origin, using the angle given.

(5) (0, 0) (0, 3) (3, 1) (0, 0)   90° clockwise

(6) (0, 0) (−2, 1) (−3, 3) (−1, 2) (0, 0)   180°

(7) (0, 0) (−1, −2) (−3, −2) (−2, 0) (0, 0)   270° clockwise

(8) (0, 0) (3, −3) (1, −3) (0, 0)   90° anticlockwise

Translations

On this page you will learn to sketch the pattern of a shape after it has been translated.

Translating a shape means moving it in a straight line.

Example

Translate the shaded shape:

1 left 6 squares (L6)

2 down 5 squares (D5)

3 left 5 squares, up 1 square (L5 U1)

4 left 2 squares, down 4 squares (L2, D4).

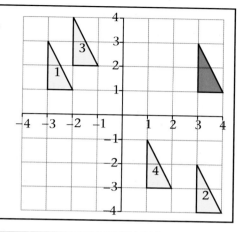

M

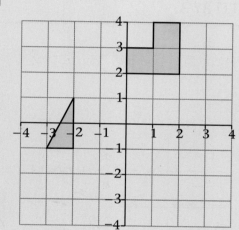

1 Copy the grid and the hexagon.

Translate the shape three times.

a) R2   b) L3   c) D3

2 Copy the grid and the triangle.

Translate the triangle three times.

a) U2   b) R4   c) L1

3 Copy the grid and the hexagon above.

Translate the shape three times.

a) L4 D2   b) L1 D3   c) R2 D1

4 Copy the grid and the triangle above.

Translate the triangle three times.

a) L1 U2   b) R3 D1   c) R4 U2

E

Plot the following triangles on grids like those above. Sketch the positions after each of the translations.

1 (1, 1), (1, 3), (2, 1)

a) R2 D3

b) L3 U1

c) L4 D3

2 (−2, 1), (−1, 3), (0, 1)

a) R3 U1

b) L1 D4

c) R4 D3

3 (1, −1), (2, −2), (0, −3)

a) R1 U4

b) L3 D1

c) L2 U5

On these pages you will enlarge shapes by a scale factor.

Example

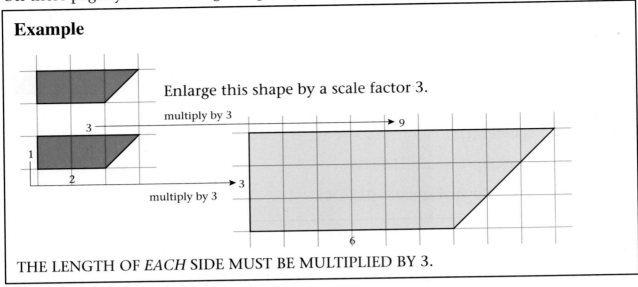

Enlarge this shape by a scale factor 3.

THE LENGTH OF *EACH* SIDE MUST BE MULTIPLIED BY 3.

Ⓜ

Enlarge these shapes by the given scale factor.

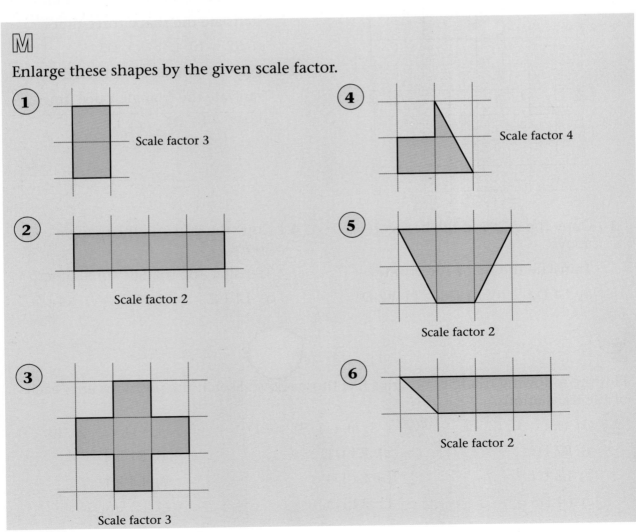

1. Scale factor 3

2. Scale factor 2

3. Scale factor 3

4. Scale factor 4

5. Scale factor 2

6. Scale factor 2

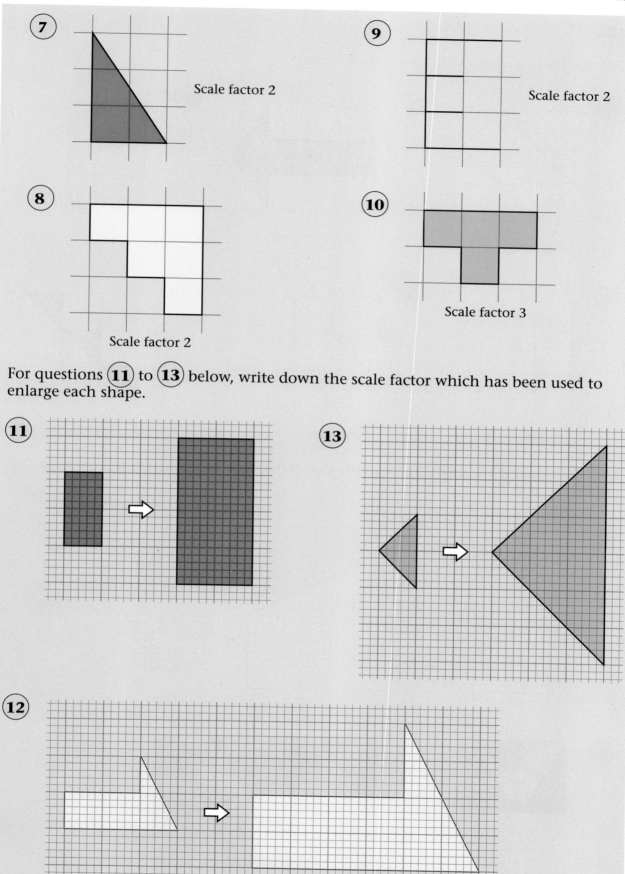

⑦ Scale factor 2

⑧ Scale factor 2

⑨ Scale factor 2

⑩ Scale factor 3

For questions ⑪ to ⑬ below, write down the scale factor which has been used to enlarge each shape.

⑪

⑬

⑫

Enlarge these shapes by the given scale factor.

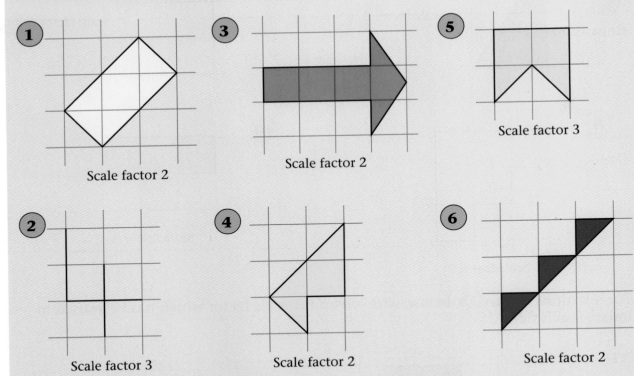

1 Scale factor 2

3 Scale factor 2

5 Scale factor 3

2 Scale factor 3

4 Scale factor 2

6 Scale factor 2

For Questions **7** and **8** below, write down the scale factor which has been used to enlarge each shape.

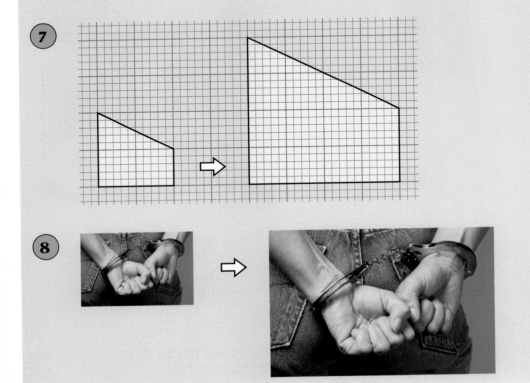

7

8

On these pages you will learn to use letters in place of numbers.

Reminder

Write down an EXPRESSION for the PERIMETER of this rectangle.

Perimeter means the total distance around the edge of the shape.

The perimeter is $l + w + l + w$

$$= 2l + 2w$$

M

For each shape below, find an expression for the perimeter.

1

4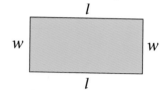

7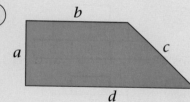

2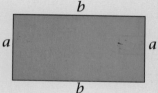

5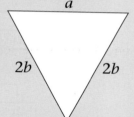

8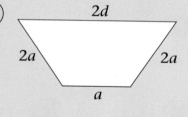

3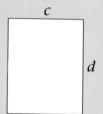

6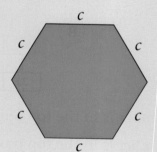

9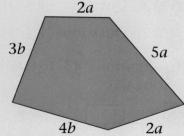

10 For each shape in Questions **1** to **9**, find the value of the perimeter if $a = 2$ cm, $b = 3$ cm, $c = 5$ cm and $d = 10$ cm.

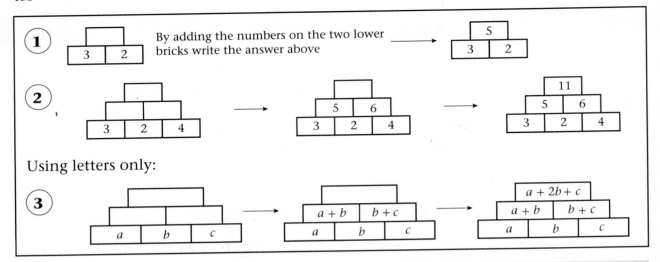

1 By adding the numbers on the two lower bricks write the answer above

2

Using letters only:

3

E

Fill in each empty box like the examples above.

1 | 3 | 4 | 7 |

5 | x | y | z |

2 | 2 | 8 | 5 |

6 | 2x | 3x | 5x |

3 | x | x | x |

7 | 2x | y | 2x |

4 | x | x | y |

8 | 3x | 2y | 4x | 2y |

9 In Question **3**, what number is in the top box if $x = 4$?

10 In Question **4**, what number is in the top box if $x = 2$ and $y = 4$?

11 In Question **5**, what number is in the top box if $x = 7$, $y = 2$ and $z = 6$?

12 In Question **7**, what number is in the top box if $x = 5$ and $y = 10$?

In Questions **13** to **16** below, find out if the number in the top brick is right (✓) or wrong (X).

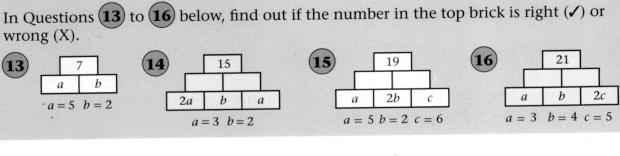

13 | 7 | over | a | b |
$a = 5$ $b = 2$

14 | 15 | over | 2a | b | a |
$a = 3$ $b = 2$

15 | 19 | over | a | 2b | c |
$a = 5$ $b = 2$ $c = 6$

16 | 21 | over | a | b | 2c |
$a = 3$ $b = 4$ $c = 5$

Equations 1

On these pages you will write equations and solve equations.

---

a) Solve $n + 5 = 9$

'Solve' means 'find the value of n'

$n = 4$ because $\boxed{4} + 5 = 9$

b) Solve $n - 3 = 6$

$n = 9$ because $\boxed{9} - 3 = 6$

c) Solve $4n = 12$

$4n$ means '$4 \times n$'

$n = 3$ because $4 \times 3 = 12$

d) Solve $3n - 5 = 16$

$\boxed{3n} - 5 = 16$
$\uparrow$

This box = 21 because $\boxed{21} - 5 = 16$

so $\boxed{3n} = 21$
$\downarrow$

$3n$ means $3 \times n$

so $3 \times n = 21$

so $n = 7$ because $3 \times \boxed{7} = 21$.

Ⓜ

Solve the equations.

① $n + 7 = 11$

② $n + 3 = 15$

③ $n - 7 = 7$

④ $n - 5 = 25$

⑤ $6 + n = 100$

⑥ $8 + n = 28$

⑦ $11 = n + 2$

⑧ $7 = n - 52$

⑨ $0 = n - 3$

⑩ $6 + n = 6$

⑪ $n - 11 = 11$

⑫ $14 = 5 + n$

In Questions ⑬ to ㉑, copy and fill the empty boxes.

⑬ $\boxed{3n} + 4 = 19$

$\boxed{3n} = 15$

$n = \boxed{}$

⑭ $\boxed{2n} + 6 = 18$

$\boxed{2n} = 12$

$n = \boxed{}$

⑮ $\boxed{3n} + 7 = 19$

$\boxed{3n} = \boxed{}$

$n = \boxed{}$

⑯ $\boxed{4n} + 5 = 13$

$\boxed{4n} = \boxed{}$

$n = \boxed{}$

⑰ $\boxed{3n} - 2 = 16$

$\boxed{3n} = 18$

$n = \boxed{}$

⑱ $\boxed{5n} - 6 = 14$

$\boxed{5n} = \boxed{}$

$n = \boxed{}$

⑲ $\boxed{4n} - 3 = 25$

$\boxed{4n} = \boxed{}$

$n = \boxed{}$

⑳ $\boxed{5n} + 4 = 34$

$\boxed{5n} = \boxed{}$

$n = \boxed{}$

㉑ $\boxed{3n} - 3 = 21$

$\boxed{3n} = \boxed{}$

$n = \boxed{}$

Solve the equations below:

(22) $3n = 18$

(23) $2n = 60$

(24) $5n = 40$

(25) $2n + 1 = 7$

(26) $3n + 2 = 14$

(27) $4n + 7 = 19$

(28) $3n + 2 = 17$

(29) $4n + 6 = 14$

(30) $6n + 5 = 41$

(31) $5n - 3 = 7$

(32) $3n - 4 = 11$

(33) $7n + 3 = 24$

(34) $6n + 5 = 35$

(35) $9n + 1 = 100$

(36) $3n - 5 = 10$

(37) $14 = 3n - 1$

(38) $31 = 7n + 3$

(39) $5 + 3n = 11$

Problem

Tom is thinking of a number.
When he multiplies it by 2 and adds 5, the answer is 13.
Write down an equation then work out what number Tom is thinking of.

Answer

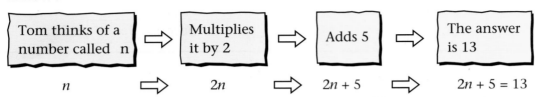

| Tom thinks of a number called n | $\Rightarrow$ | Multiplies it by 2 | $\Rightarrow$ | Adds 5 | $\Rightarrow$ | The answer is 13 |

n $\Rightarrow$ $2n$ $\Rightarrow$ $2n + 5$ $\Rightarrow$ $2n + 5 = 13$

Now solve $2n + 5 = 13$

so $\qquad 2n = 8$

so $\qquad n = 4$

Tom's number is 4.

E

In each Question below, I am thinking of a number. Write down an equation then solve it to find the number.

(1) If we multiply the number by 3 and then add 1, the answer is 25.

(2) If we multiply the number by 4 and then add 7, the answer is 31.

(3) If we multiply the number by 6 and then add 5, the answer is 23.

(4) If we multiply the number by 10 and then subtract 3, the answer is 57.

(5) If we multiply the number by 5 and then add 8, the answer is 48.

(6) If we multiply the number by 4 and then subtract 3, the answer is 13.

(7) If we double the number and add 7, the answer is 11. ('double' means 'multiply by 2')

(8) If we double the number and add 16, the answer is 30.

(9) If we double the number and subtract 20, the answer is 46.

(10) If we treble the number and subtract 7, the answer is 14. ('treble' means 'multiply by 3')

Example
Solve

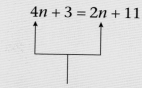

n is on both sides of the equation

What is the value of n?

Consider

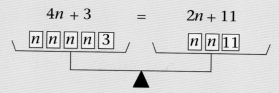

Take off $2n$ from each pan.

$$2n + 3 \quad = \quad 11$$

Take off 3 from each pan.

$$2n \quad = \quad 8$$

Each $\boxed{n}$ must equal 4 because 2 $\boxed{n}$ boxes are equal to 8 so $n = 4$.

Look again:

$$4n + 3 = 2n + 11$$

Take off $2n$ from each side of the '=' sign $2n + 3 = 11$

Take off 3 from each side of the '=' sign $\qquad 2n = 8$

$$\text{so} \qquad n = 4$$

Find the value of *n* in Questions (11) to (16):

(11)

(14)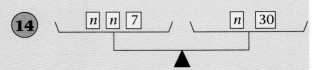

(12)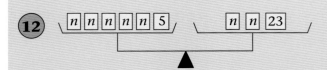

(15)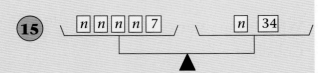

(13)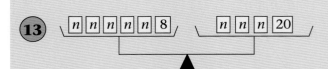

(16)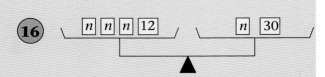

In Questions (17) to (20), copy and fill the empty boxes.

(17) $5n + 4 = 2n + 13$

$\boxed{3n} + 4 = 13$

$3n = \boxed{}$

$n = \boxed{}$

(18) $7n + 2 = 3n + 34$

$\boxed{} + 2 = 34$

$\boxed{} = 32$

$n = \boxed{}$

(19) $5n + 3 = 2n + 33$

$\boxed{} + 3 = 33$

$\boxed{} = 30$

$n = \boxed{}$

(20) $9n + 11 = 3n + 41$

$\boxed{} + 11 = 41$

$\boxed{} = \boxed{}$

$n = \boxed{}$

Solve the equations below:

(21) $4n + 3 = n + 9$

(22) $7n + 1 = 6n + 8$

(23) $3n + 7 = n + 15$

(24) $5n + 1 = 3n + 13$

(25) $6n + 6 = 3n + 24$

(26) $10n + 3 = 5n + 48$

(27) $6n - 1 = 3n + 8$

(28) $5n - 4 = 2n + 5$

Substitution and Formulas 2

On these pages you will learn how to put numbers in place of letters in expressions and formulas.

Remember

$7a$ means $7 \times a$

ab means $a \times b$

b^2 means $b \times b$

$3a - 4$ means '$3 \times a$ then subtract 4'

$2(a + 7)$ means '$a + 7$ then multiply by 2'

$\frac{a}{b}$ means $a \div b$

Examples

Find the value of each expression when $a = 2$, $b = 1$ and $c = 4$.

$2a + 3 = 2 \times 2 + 3 = 4 + 3 = 7$

$bc = 1 \times 4 = 4$

$b^2 = 1 \times 1 = 1$

$b(a + c) = 1 \times (2 + 4) = 1 \times 6 = 6$

$\frac{c}{a} = 4 \div 2 = 2$

Remember BODMAS. The order of operations is Brackets then $\div \times + -$

M

In Questions (1) to (16) find the value of each expression when $x = 2$
$y = 4$
$z = 7$.

(1) $3x$

(2) $x + y + z$

(3) $4x - z$

(4) $2y + 3z$

(5) $4y - 2$

(6) $3x + 2z$

(7) $4x + 3y + 3z$

(8) x^2

(9) z^2

(10) $x^2 + y^2$

(11) $2(x + 3)$

(12) $\frac{y - x}{x}$

(13) $y(2x + z)$

(14) $z(3y - z)$

(15) $\frac{3x + y}{x}$

(16) $\frac{8x}{y}$

In Questions (17) to (32) find the value of each expression when $a = 5$
$b = 4$
$c = 1$.

(17) $5a - c$

(18) $2b + a$

(19) $4b + c$

(20) $5b + 10$

(21) $a + b + c$

(22) $b - c$

(23) $25 + 5b$

(24) a^2

(25) $a^2 + b^2$

(26) $ac + b$

(27) $6 - 2c$

(28) $2(a - c)$

(29) $a(c + b)$

(30) $\frac{b + c}{a}$

(31) $\frac{a - b}{c}$

(32) abc

In Questions ③ to ④ find the value of each expression

(33) $2x + 1$, if $x = 4$ **(37)** $10 + a$, if $a = 5$ **(41)** $4 + 3c$, if $c = 6$

(34) $3x - 1$, if $x = 2$ **(38)** $7 - a$, if $a = 4$ **(42)** $20 - 2c$, if $c = 7$

(35) $5x - 2$, if $x = 3$ **(39)** $12 - b$, if $b = 6$ **(43)** $4(a - 9)$, if $a = 12$

(36) $4x + 3$, if $x = 3$ **(40)** $16 + b$, if $b = 3$ **(44)** $x^2 + 7$, if $x = 8$

In Questions **(1)** to **(6)** use the formula $V = lwh$ to find the Volume of each cuboid (box).

(*l* means length, *w* means width, *h* means height)

(1)

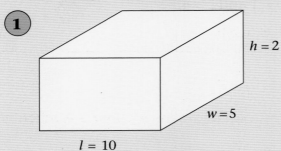

$h = 2$

$w = 5$

$l = 10$

(4)

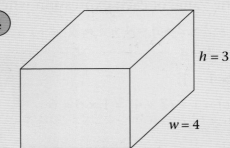

$h = 3$

$w = 4$

$l = 10$

(2) length = 5, width = 4, height = 3   **(5)** $l = 5$, $w = 5$, $h = 8$

(3) $l = 8$, $w = 3$, $h = 5$ **(6)** $l = 12$, $w = 10$, $h = 4$

In Questions **(7)** to **(12)** use the formula $y = mx + c$ to find the value of y.

(This means 'work out $m \times x$ then add c')

(7) $m = 3$, $x = 2$, $c = 4$ **(10)** $m = 10$, $x = 2$, $c = 21$

(8) $m = 6$, $x = 5$, $c = 10$ **(11)** $m = 20$, $x = 5$, $c = 63$

(9) $m = 4$, $x = 5$, $c = 6$ **(12)** $m = 4$, $x = 15$, $c = 40$

In Questions **(13)** to **(20)** you are given a formula.

Find the value of the letter required in each Question.

(13) $x = 3y + 2$ Find x, when $y = 4$

(14) $a = 4b + 1$ Find a, when $b = 5$

(15) $g = 8h + 7$ Find g, when $h = 6$

(16) $f = 5g - 3$ Find f, when $g = 7$

(17) $v = 3(5w - 6)$ Find v, when $w = 2$

(18) $x = 3(y - 4)$ Find x, when $y = 8$

(19) $a = 100 - 5b$ Find a, when $b = 20$

(20) $t = \dfrac{4u + 3}{5}$ Find t, when $u = 3$

On these pages you will learn about hypotheses and discuss related questions.

A hypothesis is 'something you think could be true.'

Example

'Children use computers more than adults.'

This may be true or may not be true.

To test this hypothesis, we must collect data.

What data is needed? Discuss with your teacher.

Where will you find the data? Discuss with your teacher.

How do you collect the data? Discuss with your teacher.

M/E

For each of the following hypotheses, work in a group or discuss with your teacher:

a) What data is needed?

b) Where will you find the data?

c) How do you collect the data?

1. 'Doing more exercise will make you thinner.'

2. 'Eastenders is the most popular Soap on TV.'

3. 'More Year 8 children eat cereal for breakfast than any other food.'

4. 'More people holiday in Spain than in the U.S.A.'

5. 'Children eat more sweets than adults.'

6. 'More people own dogs than cats.'

Hypothesis

'Children watch more TV than adults.'

When discussing this before in Section M, many questions may have been asked. For example:

1. What counts as 'watching TV'? Does it count if you are just in the room?

2. Can people remember what they watched 24 hours ago?

3. Are people going to answer honestly?

4. What about watching videos?

These are called 'related questions' and need to be thought about.

Discuss these and any other related questions with your teacher.

On these pages you will find the mean, median, mode and range of data.

The marks achieved by 6 pupils in a test were:

6, 7, 3, 2, 5, 7

a) Mean mark = $\dfrac{6 + 7 + 3 + 2 + 5 + 7}{6}$ = 5

b) Arrange the marks in order: 2 3 5 6 7 7

The median is the half-way number

Median = $\dfrac{5 + 6}{2}$ = 5.5

c) Mode = 7 because there are more 7's than any other number.

d) Range = highest number – lowest number

$\qquad$ = $\qquad$ 7 $\qquad$ – $\qquad$ 2

$\qquad$ = $\qquad$ 5

Ⓜ

Copy and fill the empty boxes.

(1) The marks achieved by 9 children in a test.   6   7   10   8   5   8   6   5   8

The *range* is the highest mark ☐ – the lowest mark ☐ = ☐ .

The *mode* is the most common value, which is ☐ .

The *median* is the middle value when the numbers are arranged in size order

–   –   –   –   –   –   –   –

The *mean* is the total marks ☐ ÷ 9 (the number of children) = ☐ .

(2) The number of goals scored by a school football team in their 13 matches.

3   1   4   0   1   2   8   1   4   7   2   1   5

Range ☐   Mode ☐   Median ☐   Mean ☐

(3) The ages of 11 dogs in a park.   3   8   13   4   2   1   8   4   10   5   8

Range ☐   Mode ☐   Median ☐   Mean ☐

(4) The daily hours of sunshine recorded in one week in June.

Range ☐   Median ☐

Mode ☐   Mean ☐

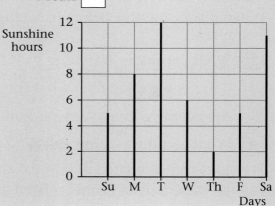

E

You may use a calculator to work out the questions below.

1 15 children run a race. Their times (in seconds) are recorded below:

14.8	15.1	15.2	14.4	14.3
14.3	14.8	14	15.2	14.6
14.7	13.9	14.3	15	14.4

Calculate the mean average time.

2 25 children are asked how many presents they got for their birthdays. The numbers are given below:

6	5	3	8	3
4	4	9	2	4
7	2	1	4	2
3	8	7	4	1
2	10	4	3	7

Calculate the mean number of presents.

3 30 children got the following percentage marks in a mathematics test:

62	54	48	72	51	86
47	68	59	46	84	51
53	53	94	58	47	48
71	62	91	55	63	67
56	82	63	47	62	51

Calculate the mean percentage mark.

4 Find the median percentage mark for the marks given in Question **3**.

5 Find the range for the marks given in Question **3**.

6 Write down 3 numbers with a mean of 6.

7 Write down 3 different numbers with a mean of 6.

8 Write down 6 numbers with a range of 10.

9 Write down 5 numbers with a median of 7.

10 The 5 numbers below have a mean of 6.

What is the value of x?

7	5	8	x	6

11 The 8 numbers below have a mode of 3.

What is the value of x?

3	8	3	9
x	8	2	5

12 20 children hold their breath for as long as they can. The times (in seconds) are given below:

42	48	41	54	42
47	53	51	53	37
39	35	48	48	53
52	37	41	39	45

Calculate

a) the mean time

b) the median time

c) the range.

On these pages you will learn to interpret pie charts and to draw pie charts.

• How children go to a school in the Alps.

$\frac{1}{2}$ of the children walk to school

$\frac{1}{4}$ of the children swim to school

$\frac{1}{4}$ of the children hang glide to school

• People in a Spanish jail.

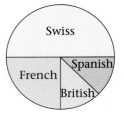

$\frac{1}{8}$ of the people were Spanish

$\frac{1}{8}$ of the people were British

$\frac{1}{4}$ of the people were French

$\frac{1}{2}$ of the people were Swiss

Ⓜ

①

The pie chart shows the contents of a bar of chocolate.

a) What fraction of the contents is chocolate?

b) What fraction of the contents is toffee?

c) If the total weight of the packet is 400 g, what is the weight of nuts?

② In a survey children said what pets they had at home.

a) What fraction of the children had a hamster?

b) What fraction of the children had a dog?

c) 40 children took part in the survey.

   How many of these children had a pet spider?

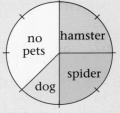

③ In another survey children were asked what *pests* they had at home. $\frac{1}{3}$ of the children said, 'my sister'.

What angle would you draw for the 'my sister' sector on a pie chart?

④ The pie chart shows the results of a survey in which 80 people were asked how they travelled to work. Copy this table and fill it in.

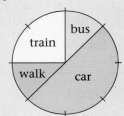

Method	car	walk	train	bus
Number of people				

5 In 2008 and 2009 children were asked in a survey to say which country they would most like to go to for a holiday. The pie charts show the results.

100 children answered in
each year
Countries in the 'others' section had
only one or two votes each.

2008   2009

a) Which was the most popular country in the 2008 survey?

b) Which country was less popular in 2009 than in 2008?

c) *Roughly* how many children said 'Jamaica' in the 2008 survey?

6 A hidden observer watched Philip in a 40 minute maths lesson.

He spent: 20 minutes talking to a friend,

             10 minutes getting ready to work,

             5 minutes working,

             5 minutes packing up.

Draw and label a pie chart to show Philip's lesson.

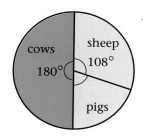

Example

A farmer has 5 cows, 3 sheep and 2 pigs. Show this on a pie chart.

Method

a) Add all the numbers:

5 + 3 + 2 = 10 animals.

b) Whole angle in a pie chart = 360°

This must be split between 10 animals.

Angle for each animal = 360° ÷ 10

                       = 36°.

c) Angle for cows = 5 × 36° = 180°

Angle for sheep = 3 × 36° = 108°

Angle for pigs = 2 × 36° = 72°

Teachers note: The answer book has a section on using a spreadsheet on a computer to draw pie charts and bar charts.

E

1) Some people were asked what they had for breakfast. The answers are shown below:

Breakfast	frequency (number of people)
toast	9
cereal	15
egg	2
nothing	10

a) Add up how many people were asked.

b) Work out the angle for each person to help draw a pie chart. [i.e. 360 ÷ (total number of people)]

c) Work out the angle for each type of breakfast and draw a pie chart.

2) Some people were asked what their favourite TV 'Soap' was. The answers are shown below:

Soap	Frequency
Eastenders	30
Neighbours	20
Coronation Street	32
Emmerdale	8

a) Add up how many people were asked.

b) Work out the angle for each person to help draw a pie chart. [i.e. 360 ÷ (total number of people)]

c) Work out the angle for each 'Soap' and draw a pie chart.

In Questions 3, 4, 5 work out the angle for each item and draw a pie chart.

3) Number of programmes per night

Programme	Frequency
News	2
Soap	5
Comedy	4
Drama	5
Film	2

4) Pupils' favourite sports.

Sport	Frequency
Rugby	5
Football	7
Tennis	4
Squash	2
Athletics	3
Swimming	3

5) Periods per subject.

Subject	Frequency
Maths	5
English	5
Science	6
Humanities	4
Arts	4
Others	16

On these pages you will learn how to put data into a stem and leaf diagram and how to interpret a stem and leaf diagram.

Data can be displayed in groups in a stem and leaf diagram. Here are the marks of 20 girls in a science test.

47	53	71	55	28	40	45	62	57	64
33	48	59	61	73	37	75	26	68	39

We will put the marks into groups 20–29, 30–39.:... 70–79.

We will choose the tens digit as the 'stem' and the units as the 'leaf'.

The first four marks are shown [47, 53, 71, 55]

Stem (tens)	Leaf (units)
2	
3	
4	7
5	3 5
6	
7	1

The complete diagram is below . . . . . and then with the leaves in numerical order:

Stem	Leaf
2	8 6
3	3 7 9
4	7 0 5 8
5	3 5 7 9
6	2 4 1 8
7	1 3 5

Stem	Leaf
2	6 8
3	3 7 9
4	0 5 7 8
5	3 5 7 9
6	1 2 4 8
7	1 3 5

The diagram shows the shape of the distribution. It is also easy to find the mode, the median and the range.

Ⓜ

① The marks of 24 children in a test are shown

41	23	35	15	40	39	47	29
52	54	45	27	28	36	48	51
59	65	42	32	46	53	66	38

Draw a stem and leaf diagram. The first three entries are shown.

Stem	Leaf
1	
2	3
3	5
4	1
5	
6	

2) Draw a stem and leaf diagram for each set of data below

a)

24	52	31	55	40	37	58	61	25	46
44	67	68	75	73	28	20	59	65	39

b)

30	41	53	22	72	54	35	47
44	67	46	38	59	29	47	28

Stem	Leaf
2	
3	
4	
5	
6	
7	

3) For each set of data below, draw an unordered stem and leaf diagram then draw a second stem and leaf diagram that is properly ordered.

a) The midday temperatures for Wells in June were:

18	23	24	22	19	17	16	21	23	25
21	19	17	18	22	21	24	20	23	21
25	28	27	30	27	23	19	18	23	25

b) The scores in a French test were:

37	49	27	67	37	19	87	45	62
39	34	47	43	48	64	29	41	38
52	56	48	61	68	43	51		

E

1) Here is the stem and leaf diagram showing the masses, in kg, of some people on a bus.

a) Write down the range of the masses
b) How many people were on the bus?
c) What is the median mass?

Stem (tens)	Leaf (units)
3	3 7
4	1 2 7 7 8
5	1 6 8 9
6	0 3 7
7	4 5
8	2

In Questions **2)**, **3)**, **4)** find a) the range
b) the median

2)

Stem (tens)	Leaf (units)
2	1 4
3	0 3 6
4	4 4 7 9
5	3 6

3)

Stem	Leaf
5	1 4
6	3 5 8
7	0 1 6 8
8	2 4 7
9	5

4)

Stem	Leaf
3	5
4	2 3 4
5	1 5 7
6	8 8 9
7	5

On these pages you will find things out from different charts.

1 In a survey children were asked to name their favourite sport.

a) What was the most popular sport?

b) How many children chose Athletics?

c) How many children took part in the survey?

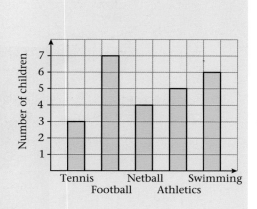

2 Here is a *bar-line graph* showing the number of children in the families of children in a school.

a) How many families had three children?

b) How many families were there altogether?

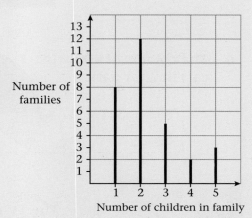

3 This table shows the number of different sorts of snacks sold by a shop.

a) How many snacks were sold on Thursday?

b) Each Aero costs 22 p. How much was spent on Aeros in the whole week?

	Mon	Tu	Wed	Th	Fri
Mars	3	1	0	0	3
Snickers	0	4	1	2	2
Twix	2	2	1	3	4
Aero	5	0	0	1	4
Crunchie	2	3	4	1	1
Kit Kat	5	0	2	1	1

In Questions 4 to 7, copy and complete the table using the information on the pie chart.

4 The ice cream flavours chosen by 32 customers of a seaside cafe.

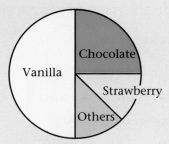

Flavour	Customers
Chocolate	
Strawberry	
Vanilla	
Others	

5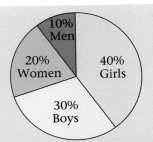

150 people at a swimming pool.

Group	Number
Boys	
Girls	
Men	
Women	

6 The colours of 400 cars in a car park.

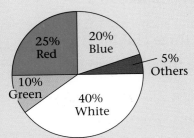

Colours	Cars
Blue	
Green	
Red	
White	
Others	

7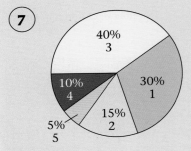

The TV channels watched by 120 viewers.

Channel	Viewers
Channel 1	
Channel 2	
Channel 3	
Channel 4	
Channel 5	

8 In a survey 40 girls and 60 boys were asked how they had spent their leisure time the previous evening. These are the results.

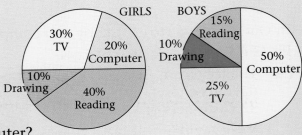

a) How many boys did some drawing?

b) How many girls played on the computer?

c) How many more girls than boys chose to read a book?

d) Did more boys or girls choose to watch TV?

E

1 Look at the bar chart below:

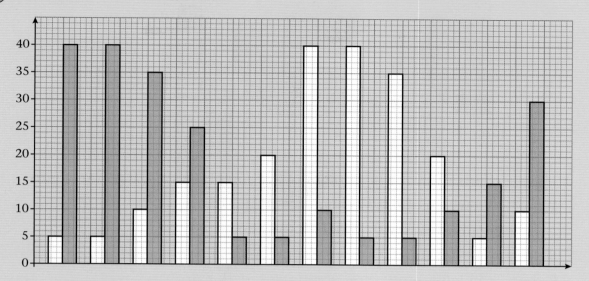

Think about then discuss the following Questions with your teacher:

a) What could the horizontal axis mean?

b) What could the numbers on the vertical axis mean?

c) Why are the bars shaded in 2 different ways?

d) What might the title of the graph be?

2

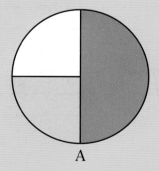

A

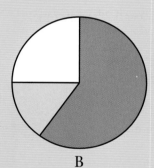

B

Look at the pie charts above.

a) Why might there be 2 pie charts?

b) What could the title of the charts be?

Discuss with your teacher.

c) Here are 2 more pie charts.

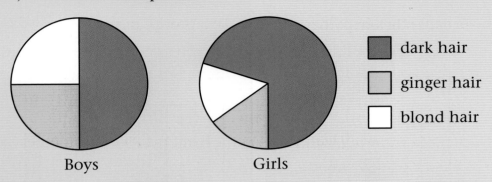

Boys   Girls

The pie charts show the hair colour of a group of boys and a group of girls.

Write down which of the 3 statements below is true:

A there are more girls with dark hair than boys.

B there are fewer girls with blond hair than boys.

C there is a higher proportion of girls with dark hair than boys.

Discuss with your teacher.

d) If there are 100 boys and 50 girls, do more boys have dark hair than girls or not?

Discuss with your teacher.

3   In a survey 320 people on an aircraft and 800 people on a ferry were asked to state where they lived.

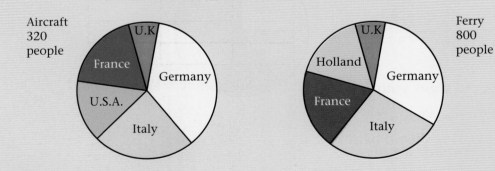

Aircraft 320 people

Ferry 800 people

Jill looked at the charts and said 'There were about the same number of people from Italy on the aircraft and on the ferry'. Explain why Jill is wrong.

On these pages you will state a hypothesis, collect data, process data and interpret the data.

Task

Are you more accurate at throwing with your writing hand than with your other hand?

1 Write down a *hypothesis* by choosing A, B or C below:

A People in my class are *more* accurate at throwing with their writing hand than with their other hand.

B People in my class throw with their writing hand to about the *same* accuracy as with their other hand.

C People in my class are *less* accurate at throwing with their writing hand than with their other hand.

2 Discuss with your teacher how you can collect data to test your hypothesis.

One way is written below:

'Each person in the class throws a screwed-up ball of paper into a rubbish bin from a fixed distance. Throw five with each hand and collect results for the whole class.'

Write the data in a table.

One possible table is shown below:

On Target	Writing Hand	Other Hand
0		
1		
2		
3		
4		
5		

3 Draw a chart to show your findings.

Discuss this with your teacher.

A possible chart is shown below:

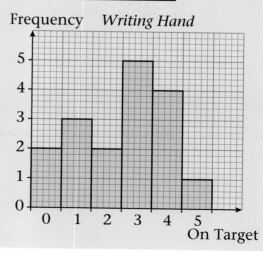

4 Use a calculator to find the mean average number of shots on target with the 'writing hand'.

Use a calculator to find the mean average number of shots on target with the 'other hand'.

Discuss with your teacher.

5 Copy and complete the conclusion below:

'The average number of shots on target with the writing hand is. . . . . .than the average number of shots on target with the other hand.'

By looking at this and the chart(s), was your hypothesis true or false?

6 If you had more time, you could look in more detail at the accuracy of shots between boys and girls or between Year 7 pupils and Year 8 pupils. Maybe change how far you were throwing or what you were throwing?

E

Use a computer to do the Data Handling Project in Section M.

In particular, try making bar charts and pie charts.

Ask your teacher how to find mean averages using a computer.

1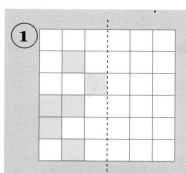

Copy this diagram onto squared paper. Shade *6 more squares* so that the dashed line is a *line of symmetry*.

You may use a mirror or tracing paper to help.

2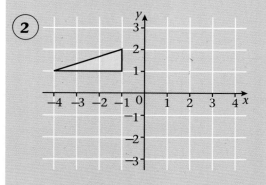

Copy this grid and triangle.

Translate the triangle

3 units right and

2 units down.

3 Use the same grid as Question **2**.

Look at the triangle given in Question **2** and *reflect* it in the x-axis.

4 The shaded rectangle is reflected in the dotted mirror line.

Point P stays in the same place.

Write down the coordinates of the place where point Q is reflected to.

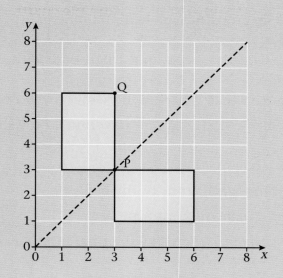

5

Write down the order of rotational symmetry of this shape.

6 Copy the shape below onto squared paper.
Enlarge the shape by a scale factor 3.

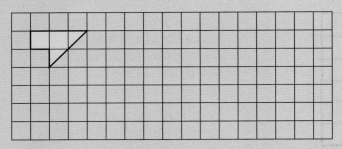

7 The shaded rectangle
is rotated 90° clockwise.

Point P stays in the
same place.

Write down the coordinates
of the place where point Q
is rotated to.

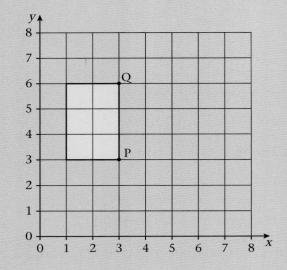

8 To make green paint, you can mix blue paint with yellow paint.

To make 'Ghastly' green, mix 1 part blue with 3 parts yellow

   a) To make 'Ghastly' green, how much yellow should I mix with 200 ml of blue?

   b) To make 'Ghastly' green, how much blue should I mix with 900 ml of yellow?

9 Tara has a bag of coins.

n is the number of coins in the bag.

Tara puts *4 more coins* into the bag.

Write an *expression* to show the total number of coins in the bag now.

10 Again, Tara has n coins in a bag.

She puts more coins into the bag so that there are *twice as many* coins.

She then *takes 3 coins out of her bag.*

Write an expression to show the total number of coins in the bag now.

11 The weights below are given in kilograms
The weights are balanced.
What is the value of x.

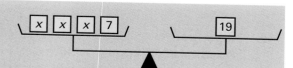

12 When 2y – 11 = 7, work out the value of y.

13 Find the value of 5a – 3b when a = 6 and b = 4.

14 Julie is using the formula $s = \frac{d}{t}$ to find the speed s when she knows the distance d and the time t.

Find the value of s when d = 28 and t = 4.

15 The scores in a maths test were:

56	42	58	38	39	38	55	90	68
77	41	63	81	41	42	58	91	61
61	63	72	77	41	61	82	73	55

Draw an *ordered stem and leaf diagram* for this set of data.

16 There are 40 children altogether in a class.

Using the pie chart,

a) *How many* of the children are *boys*?

b) What *percentage* of the children are boys?

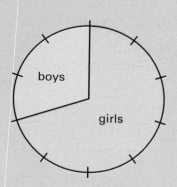

17 Sunil has 5 test marks:

    72   63   71   84   77

Faye has 5 test marks:

    51   89   64   73   76

Who has the highest *median* mark and *by how much*?

(18) 18 people were asked what their favourite fruit was.
The answers are shown below:

Fruit	Frequency (number of people)
Apple	6
Strawberry	8
Peach	3
Banana	1

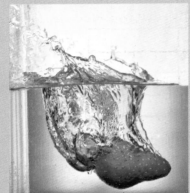

a) Add up how many people were asked.

b) Work out the angle for each person to help draw a pie chart.
[i.e. 360° ÷ (total number of people)]

c) Work out the angle for each type of fruit and *use a protractor* to draw a pie chart.

(19) Poppy spends the money below on each day of her holiday.

Sunday	Monday	Tuesday	Wednesday	Thursday	Friday
£15	£16	£5	£21	£8	£13

Poppy said 'My *mean average* spending *each day* was £12.'
Show if this is true or false.

(20) A shop kept a tally chart to show which type of video they sold one weekend.

	Saturday	Sunday
comedy	卌 卌 ||	卌 卌 卌
drama	卌 |||	卌 卌 |||
horror	卌		卌 卌
science-fiction	卌 卌	卌 |||

a) How many *comedy* videos were sold on *Sunday*?

b) Altogether, how many videos were sold on *Saturday*?

c) How *many more drama* videos were bought on *Sunday* than on *Saturday*?

On this page you will try to solve a crossnumber puzzle.

Copy the grid below.

Fill in the grid using the clues.

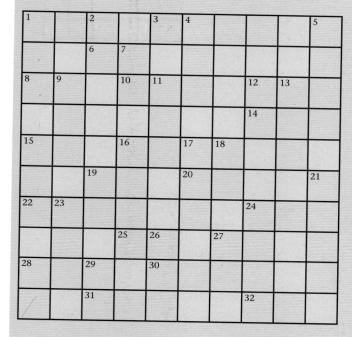

Clues across

1 536 + 219

3 2511 – 699

6 5 × 15

8 637 ÷ 7

10 591 ÷ 3

12 64 × 8

14 11 × 11 × 4

15 101 – 39 + 7

16 2000 – 238

19 3 × 14

20 180 – 135

22 809 × 7

24 96 + 79

25 182 – 139

27 3 × 3 × 3

28 1000 – 599

30 4657 + 2732

31 15 × 5 × 3

32 2 × 30

Clues down

1 9 × 9 × 9

2 3 × 19

4 1001 – 114

5 8 × 128

7 100 – 49

9 13 × 13

11 1000 – 83

12 3 × 18

13 4 × 45

15 5 × 127

16 9999 – 8765

17 8 × 80

18 1000 ÷ 40

19 19 + 17 + 10

21 3 × 50 × 10

23 6100 ÷ 10

24 2000 – 204

26 750 – 375

27 112 ÷ 4

28 7 × 7

29 132 ÷ 11

Mental Strategies 3

On these pages you will practise a mixture of problems in your head using decimals, fractions and percentages.

Ⓜ

In Questions **1** to **5** find the change from £10 if you spend:

1 £6.80 **3** £6.70 **5** £2.15

2 £4.30 **4** £3.35

In Questions **6** to **10** change the number into a fraction.

6 0.07 **8** 31% **10** 0.83

7 0.4 **9** 9%

Work out

11 $\sqrt{81}$ **14** $\sqrt{1} + \sqrt{25}$

12 $\sqrt{16}$ **15** $\sqrt{100} - \sqrt{49}$

13 $\sqrt{64}$

In Questions **16** to **20** find the change from £10 if you spend:

16 £1.79 **18** £3.64 **20** £0.47

17 £3.42 **19** £2.88

In Questions **21** to **25** change the number into a percentage.

21 $\frac{3}{100}$ **23** 0.04 **25** $\frac{1}{4}$

22 $\frac{43}{100}$ **24** 0.9

Work out

26 7^2 **29** $5^2 + 4^2$

27 6^2 **30** $1^2 + 2^2 + 3^2$

28 20^2

31 Which is larger?

$\frac{1}{4}$ of £80 or 10% of £180

32 Which is larger?

$\frac{1}{3}$ of £27 or 20% of £50

33 Which is larger?

20% of £60 or $\frac{1}{8}$ of £72

34 Which is larger?

5% of £120 or $\frac{2}{5}$ of £20

35 Find the cost of five drinks at 99p each.

In Questions **36** to **40** change the number into a percentage.

36 $\frac{3}{4}$ **38** $\frac{4}{5}$ **40** $\frac{7}{25}$

37 $\frac{1}{5}$ **39** $\frac{3}{20}$

Work out

41 $\frac{3}{5} + \frac{1}{5}$ **43** $\frac{9}{11} - \frac{6}{11}$ **45** $\frac{1}{2} + \frac{1}{4}$

42 $\frac{9}{10} - \frac{5}{10}$ **44** $\frac{5}{8} + \frac{2}{8}$

E

1. Write $\frac{9}{100}$ as a decimal number.

2. What is $\frac{1}{4}$ of £22?

3. Work out five per cent of four hundred.

4. 68% of the children in class 8C think that motor bikes are dangerous. What percentage of the children do not think that motor bikes are dangerous?

5. If 83% of people like chocolate, what percentage do not like chocolate?

6. What is the cost of two items at two pounds ninety-nine pence each?

7. Sophie bought a drink for 79p, food for £3.82 and a hairbrush for £2.99. How much change from £10 would she have?

8. On a very hot day Tom bought sunglasses for £13.50 and a cold drink for 85p. How much change from £20 would he have?

9. Tim finds a bike which costs £340. The bike shop reduces the price by 20%. How much will the bike now cost?

10. Hannah wants to buy a trampoline which costs £500. Hannah must pay 5% of £500 and her parents will pay the rest. How much will Hannah pay?

11. What is $\frac{3}{5}$ of £40?

12. Matt is given $\frac{1}{8}$ of £56. Jade is given $\frac{2}{3}$ of £12. Who is given the most money?

13. Michelle got thirty out of fifty on a test. What percentage did she get?

14. In a class of 20 children, 11 are girls. What percentage of the class are girls?

15. Asif is 1.62 m tall. Harriet is 1.49 m tall. How much taller is Asif than Harriet?

16. How many halves are there altogether in four and a half?

17. Write down the square root of 81.

18. Work out seven squared subtract four squared.

19. The side of a square is six centimetres. What is the area of the square?

20. The area of a square is 100 cm². How long is one side of the square?

On these pages you will add and subtract more fractions.

Remember

Fractions can be added or subtracted when they have the same denominator (bottom number).

Examples

$$\frac{2}{7} + \frac{4}{7} = \frac{6}{7} \qquad\qquad \frac{8}{11} - \frac{3}{11} = \frac{5}{11}$$

Sometimes the denominators have to be made the same before adding or subtracting. Use equivalent fractions.

Examples

$$\frac{3}{6} + \left(\frac{1}{3}\right) = \frac{3}{6} + \left(\frac{2}{6}\right) = \frac{5}{6}$$

$$\frac{7}{8} - \left(\frac{1}{4}\right) = \frac{7}{8} - \left(\frac{2}{8}\right) = \frac{5}{8}$$

Work out

(1) $\frac{1}{7} + \frac{2}{7}$

(2) $\frac{1}{6} + \frac{4}{6}$

(3) $\frac{5}{8} + \frac{1}{8}$

(4) $\frac{2}{9} + \frac{3}{9}$

(5) $\frac{3}{10} + \frac{4}{10}$

(6) $\frac{3}{11} + \frac{2}{11}$

Draw fraction charts, using squared paper, and use them with the remaining questions

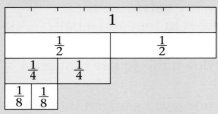
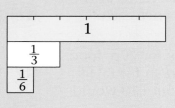
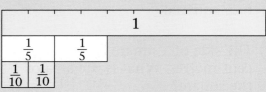

In Questions **(7)** to **(15)** fill in the missing numbers.

(7) $\frac{1}{2} = \frac{}{8}$

(8) $\frac{2}{3} = \frac{}{6}$

(9) $\frac{3}{5} = \frac{}{10}$

(10) $\frac{3}{4} = \frac{}{8}$

(11) $\frac{4}{5} = \frac{}{10}$

(12) $\frac{1}{3} = \frac{}{6}$

(13) $\frac{1}{2} = \frac{}{10}$

(14) $\frac{1}{4} = \frac{2}{}$

(15) $\frac{8}{10} = \frac{}{5}$

Work out

(16) $\frac{1}{4} + \frac{1}{2}$

(17) $\frac{1}{6} + \frac{2}{3}$

(18) $\frac{3}{8} + \frac{1}{2}$

(19) $\frac{3}{8} + \frac{1}{4}$

(20) $\frac{4}{5} + \frac{1}{10}$

(21) $\frac{2}{5} + \frac{3}{10}$

(22) $\frac{7}{8} - \frac{1}{2}$

(23) $\frac{2}{3} - \frac{1}{6}$

(24) $\frac{1}{2} - \frac{1}{8}$

(25) $\frac{3}{5} - \frac{1}{10}$

(26) $\frac{3}{4} - \frac{3}{8}$

(27) $\frac{5}{6} - \frac{1}{3}$

(28) $\frac{1}{5} + \frac{1}{10}$

(29) $\frac{1}{8} + \frac{1}{16}$

(30) $\frac{1}{10} + \frac{1}{20}$

(31) Joe gave $\frac{1}{8}$ of his sweets to his brother and $\frac{1}{4}$ of his sweets to his sister. What fraction did he give away altogether?

(32) Kate gave $\frac{1}{10}$ of her toys to a friend and $\frac{1}{5}$ of her toys to her sister. What fraction of her toys does she still have?

• To work out $\frac{1}{2} + \frac{1}{5}$ we have to change *both* fractions so that they have the same denominator (bottom number).

So $\frac{1}{2} + \frac{1}{5}$

$= \frac{5}{10} + \frac{2}{10}$ (Think: 'What number do 2 and 5 go into?')

$= \frac{7}{10}$

• To work out $\frac{3}{4} - \frac{1}{6}$ we have to change *both* fractions

So $\frac{3}{4} - \frac{1}{6}$

$= \frac{9}{12} - \frac{2}{12}$ (Think: 'What number do 4 and 6 go into?')

$= \frac{7}{12}$

E

(1) Copy and complete these calculations

a) $\frac{1}{2} + \frac{2}{5}$

$= \frac{5}{10} + \frac{4}{10}$

$=$

b) $\frac{3}{5} - \frac{1}{2}$

$= \frac{\square}{10} - \frac{\square}{10}$

$=$

c) $\frac{1}{2} - \frac{1}{5}$

$= \frac{\square}{10} - \frac{\square}{10}$

$=$

(2) Copy and complete these calculations

a) $\frac{1}{3} + \frac{2}{5}$

$= \frac{\square}{15} + \frac{6}{15}$

$=$

b) $\frac{1}{2} + \frac{1}{7}$

$= \frac{\square}{14} + \frac{\square}{14}$

$=$

c) $\frac{2}{5} + \frac{1}{4}$

$= \frac{8}{20} + \frac{\square}{20}$

$=$

3 Work out

a) $\frac{1}{3} + \frac{1}{7}$

Think: What do 3 and 7
go into?

b) $\frac{1}{5} + \frac{1}{6}$

Think: What do 5 and 6
go into?

4 These diagrams illustrate the addition $\frac{1}{4} + \frac{1}{3}$.

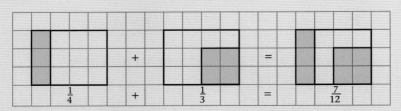

$$\frac{1}{4} \quad + \quad \frac{1}{3} \quad = \quad \frac{7}{12}$$

Copy the diagrams below, and shade in the diagrams to show the addition $\frac{1}{12} + \frac{1}{4}$.

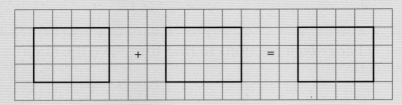

5 Work out

a) $\frac{1}{2} + \frac{1}{3}$

b) $\frac{2}{3} - \frac{1}{2}$

c) $\frac{2}{3} + \frac{1}{4}$

d) $\frac{1}{6} + \frac{1}{4}$

e) $\frac{1}{3} + \frac{1}{4}$

f) $\frac{3}{4} - \frac{1}{3}$

6 Work out

a) $\frac{1}{3} + \frac{1}{5}$

b) $\frac{2}{5} + \frac{2}{3}$

c) $\frac{1}{4} + \frac{1}{5}$

d) $\frac{4}{5} - \frac{1}{2}$

e) $\frac{2}{3} - \frac{1}{4}$

f) $\frac{2}{3} - \frac{1}{5}$

On these pages you will learn how to use brackets, divide, multiply, add and subtract in the correct order.

Remember the word 'B O D M A S'.

a) $5 + 2 \times 3$
$= 5 + 6$
$= 11$

b) $(6 + 2) \div (5 - 1) + 9$
$= 8 \div 4 + 9$
$= 2 + 9 = 11$

M

Work out

1 a) $4 + 6 \times 2$ b) $(4 + 6) \times 2$ **5** a) $20 \div 4 + 6$ b) $20 \div (4 + 6)$

2 a) $6 + 3 \times 4$ b) $(6 + 3) \times 4$ **6** a) $30 \div 5 + 1$ b) $30 \div (5 + 1)$

3 a) $24 \div 4 + 2$ b) $24 \div (4 + 2)$ **7** a) $10 \times (2 + 5)$ b) $10 \times 2 + 5$

4 a) $32 \div 4 + 4$ b) $32 \div (4 + 4)$ **8** a) $2 \times 10 + 2$ b) $2 \times (10 + 2)$

9 a) $5 + 4 \times 3 + 3$ b) $(5 + 4) \times (3 + 3)$ c) $(5 + 4) \times 3 + 3$

10 a) $6 + 3 \times 4 + 2$ b) $(6 + 3) \times 4 + 2$ c) $(6 + 3) \times (4 + 2)$

11 a) $10 + 2 \times 5 + 5$ b) $10 + 2 \times (5 + 5)$ c) $(10 + 2) \times 5 + 5$

12 a) $6 + 24 \div 3 + 5$ b) $(6 + 24) \div 3 + 5$ c) $6 + 24 \div (3 + 5)$

13 a) $12 + 36 \div (4 + 8)$ b) $(12 + 36) \div (4 + 8)$ c) $12 + 36 \div 4 + 8$

14 a) $16 \times 3 - 2$ b) $16 \times (3 - 2)$ **16** a) $40 \div 5 + 3$ b $40 \div (5 + 3)$

15 a) $16 \div 4 - 2$ b) $16 \div (4 - 2)$ **17** a) $72 \div (6 + 3)$ b) $72 \div 6 + 3$

E

Work out

1 $7 + 2 \times 6 - 1$ **4** $(6 + 4) \times (3 + 2)$ **7** $2 + 3 + 5 \div 10$

2 $8 \div 2 + 2 \times 3$ **5** $8 + 12 \div 4 + 2$ **8** $(8 + 7) \div (1 + 2 + 3 + 4 + 5)$

3 $(9 + 3) \div 6$ **6** $(2 + 3 + 5) \div 10$

These questions involve decimals.

9 $(1.4 + 2.6) \times (3.3 + 4.7)$ **13** $(4.2 + 1.4) \div 7$ **17** $(7 + 9) \div 10 + 1.4$

10 $2.5 \times 3 + 6.5$ **14** $4.2 + 1.4 \div 7$ **18** $(2.1 + 1.9) \div (0.74 + 1.26)$

11 $0.5 \times 2.2 + 1.8$ **15** $(3.8 + 2.5) \div (2.4 + 6.6)$

12 $\left(\frac{1}{2} + 3\frac{1}{2}\right) \times (4.2 + 1.8)$ **16** $6 \div 9 + 3$

On these pages you will round off numbers and work out rough answers for calculations.

Rounding to the nearest whole number.

If the first digit after the decimal point is *5 or more* round *up*.
Otherwise round down.

$57.\underline{3} \quad \rightarrow \quad$ 57 to the nearest whole number

less than 5

$7.\underline{5} \quad \rightarrow \quad 8$

$18.\underline{3}4 \quad \rightarrow \quad 18$

$27.\underline{5}4 \quad \rightarrow \quad 28$

$23.\underline{9}1 \quad \rightarrow \quad 24$

---

1 Round off these numbers to the nearest whole number.

a) 1.8

b) 6.7

c) 12.24

d) 8.97

e) 0.68

f) 8.52

g) 6.48

h) 18.35

i) 21.62

j) 5.5

k) £8.63

l) £9.47

m) £6.52

n) £55.91

o) £106.42

2 Copy and complete the table below by rounding the decimals to the nearest whole number and working out a ROUGH answer.

a)	8.9×6.1	$\rightarrow$	9×6	$\rightarrow$	54
b)	9.7×8.2	$\rightarrow$	$10 \times$	$\rightarrow$	
c)	3.1×6.9	$\rightarrow$	$\times 7$	$\rightarrow$	
d)	7.8×8.1	$\rightarrow$	$\times$	$\rightarrow$	
e)	4.9×6.2	$\rightarrow$	$\times$	$\rightarrow$	
f)	6.6×4.2	$\rightarrow$	$\times$	$\rightarrow$	
g)	5.32×2.7	$\rightarrow$	$\times$	$\rightarrow$	
h)	7.11×2.95	$\rightarrow$	$\times$	$\rightarrow$	
i)	19.62×3.22	$\rightarrow$	$\times$	$\rightarrow$	
j)	0.88×3.21	$\rightarrow$	$\times$	$\rightarrow$	

3 If a CD costs £11.85, how much will 5 CD's cost ROUGHLY?

4 A football shirt costs £8.90. If 11 players in a football team each buy one shirt, what is the total cost ROUGHLY?

5 Hats cost £32.15 each.
ROUGHLY how much will
5 hats cost?

6 A bill of £99.70 for a curry is shared equally between
5 friends. How much ROUGHLY did each friend pay?

7 9 children each bought a 'Harry Potter' book. One 'Harry Potter' book costs
£14.85. ROUGHLY how much do the 9 children pay in total?

8 A farmer buys 50 sheep at the market each costing £29.50. ROUGHLY what was
the total cost?

E

From the table below, choose the most sensible ROUGH answer from A, B or C.

	Calculation	A	B	C
1	4×3.7	15	1.5	150
2	6×6.3	4	40	400
3	3×19.2	6	600	60
4	8×12.4	100	10	1000
5	12×2.1	2.5	25	250
6	7×5.5	400	40	4.0
7	4.2×5	2.2	22	220
8	8.6×3	25	250	2.5
9	2.2×6.3	60	15	8
10	5.9×8.1	50	5	14
11	14.8×2.2	80	30	150
12	105.9×2.7	40	300	3.5

The sign $\approx$ means 'is *roughly* equal to'.

In Questions **13** to **20** below, choose the most sensible rough answer.

Example   10% of £89 is £4 or £9 or £90

Answer | 10% of £89 $\approx$ £9 | Write all your answers like this.

13 10% of £328 is £3.30 or £33 or £330.

14 50% of £69.70 is £3.50 or £35 or £350.

15 10% of £59.90 is 60p or £60 or £6.

16 25% of £80.45 is £20 or £2 or 20p.

17 $\frac{1}{2}$ of 390 is 20 or 200 or 3.9.

18 $\frac{1}{3}$ of 62 is 2 or 200 or 20.

19 $\frac{1}{4}$ of 39 is 10 or 100 or 160.

20 $\frac{1}{5}$ of 41.6 is 20 or 8 or 4.2.

On these pages you will add and subtract decimals without using a calculator.

Ⓜ

① Copy and complete the following

a) 16.3
   + 7.7

c) 39.84
   + 11.67

e) 13.04
   + 9.49

g) 45.7
   – 14.06

b) 25.7
   + 12.9

d) 76.48
   + 13.52

f) 66.02
   + 15.88

h) 167.7
   – 29.09

② Work out

a) £10.49 + £3.74

b) £10.71 – £9.63

c) £77.84 – £29.48

d) £83.56 + £25.70

e) £139.41 + £32.63

f) £217.94 – £18.27

③ a) A boy weighing 58.3 kg is 9.35 kg heavier than his sister. How much does his sister weigh?

b) 2 brothers weigh 83.64 kg and 79.55 kg. How much is their total weight?

c) John has saved £38.46 and Mary has saved £42.35. How much have they saved together?

Ⓔ

① Work out

a) 104.6 + 29.3 + 17.7

b) 921.7 + 32.03 + 156.6

c) 351.9 + 109.06 + 229

d) 179.83 – 79.28

e) 468.11 – 95.9

f) 665.9 – 91.04

② Sarita has saved £156.82 for a holiday which costs £300. How much more must she save?

③ The weights of four cars in a scrap yard were 327 kg, 411.5 kg, 279.2 kg and 354 kg. Calculate the total weight of the four cars.

④ The maximum weight a lift can carry safely is 300 kg. 4 people weigh 67.5 kg, 92.3 kg, 78.9 kg and 72.3 kg. Would it be safe for all 4 people to get in the lift?

⑤ Fred won £500 on the Lottery. He spent £133.40, £79.86 and £88.62. How much was left over from his winnings?

On these pages you will multiply and divide numbers including decimals.

M

1 Work out

a) 259 × 32

b) 157 × 26

c) 442 × 35

d) 671 × 43

e) 762 × 26

f) 304 × 46

g) 18.6 × 3

h) 257.7 × 4

i) 20.3 × 5

j) 75.2 × 4

2 Work out

a) 552 ÷ 24

b) 972 ÷ 36

c) 792 ÷ 36

d) 637 ÷ 49

e) 19.2 ÷ 6

f) 37.6 ÷ 8

g) 54.42 ÷ 3

h) 97.88 ÷ 4

3 a) Find the cost of 6 toothbrushes each costing £1.43.

b) 5 birthday cards cost £7.45 in total. What did one card cost?

c) A car does 27.6 miles to the gallon. How far will it go on 8 gallons?

E

1 Work out

a) 517 × 86

b) 309 × 78

c) 613 × 62

d) 498 × 69

e) 567 × 43

f) 385 × 7

g) 79.3 × 8

h) 48.7 × 7

i) 76.5 × 9

j) 45.73 × 6

k) 91.66 × 8

l) 57.92 × 9

2 A balloon costs £38.75 per hour to hire.

How much will it cost to hire for:

a) 3 hours

b) 5 hours?

3 You can work out how far a car can go on 1 gallon of petrol if you 'divide the number of miles by the number of gallons'.

How far does each car below go on one gallon of petrol:

a) 260 miles on 8 gallons.

b) 202.5 miles on 9 gallons.

Metric Measures

On these pages you will learn to convert one metric unit to another.

length	mass	capacity
10 mm = 1 cm	1000 g = 1 kg	1000 ml = 1 litre
100 cm = 1 m	1000 kg = 1 tonne	
1000 m = 1 km	(1 t)	

Ⓜ

Copy and complete by writing the missing number in the box.

(1) 2000 m = ☐ km

(2) 3500 m = ☐ km

(3) 2.5 km = ☐ m

(4) 7.400 km = ☐ m

(5) 290 cm = ☐ m

(6) 147 cm = ☐ m

(7) 3.61 m = ☐ cm

(8) 0.87 m = ☐ cm

(9) 37 mm = ☐ cm

(10) 16 mm = ☐ cm

(11) 9 cm = ☐ mm

(12) 0.4 cm = ☐ mm

The next questions are about mass.

(13) 4 kg = ☐ g

(14) 2.5 kg = ☐ g

(15) 3.4 kg = ☐ g

(16) 0.17 kg = ☐ g

(17) 3100 g = ☐ kg

(18) 2250 g = ☐ kg

(19) 300 g = ☐ kg

(20) 5740 g = ☐ kg

(21) 1.75 kg = ☐ g

(22) 5.92 kg = ☐ g

(23) 8000 g = ☐ kg

(24) 1600 g = ☐ kg

Write down which metric unit you would use to measure the mass of:

(25) a bus

(26) an ear ring

(27) a jumbo jet

(28) a slice of bread

The next questions are about capacity.

(29) 7 litres = ☐ ml

(30) 3.681 litres = ☐ ml

(31) 2.930 litres = ☐ ml

(32) 0.500 litres = ☐ ml

(33) 1800 ml = ☐ litres

(34) 750 ml = ☐ litres

(35) 3100 ml = ☐ litres

(36) 600 ml = ☐ litres

(37) 6.5 litres = ☐ ml

(38) 1.8 litres = ☐ ml

(39) 2250 ml = ☐ litres

(40) 480 ml = ☐ litres

Write down which metric unit you would use to measure the capacity of:

(41) a watering can

(42) a treasure chest

(43) a medicine bottle

(44) a teardrop

E

1 Janice buys 8 shelves. Each shelf is 75 cm long. How many metres of shelving does this provide?

2 A square field has a perimeter of 3.6 km. What is the length of one side in metres?

3 Six equal lengths are cut from 2 m of string. 20 cm is left over. How long are the lengths of string?

4 Jonathan walks for 2.6 km. He rests and then walks a further 1400 m. How far does he walk altogether in kilometres?

5 At midday a shadow is 42 cm long. At 6 p.m. it is eight times longer. How long is the shadow at 6 p.m. in metres?

6 A mountain peak is 4.26 km above sea level. A climber is 549 m below the summit. How high above sea level is the climber?

Write the longest length from each pair.

7 1.8 cm   8 mm

8 0.2 cm   0.01 m

9 6.23 m   623 mm

10 90 m   0.1 km

11 3.3 cm   50 mm

12 370 m   0.04 km

13 Six identical eggs weigh 0.48 kg altogether. How much does each egg weigh in grams?

14 Samson lifts 0.31 t. Hercules lifts 43 kg less. How much does Hercules lift in kilograms?

15 An apple weighs 200 g. How much do 15 apples weigh in kilograms?

16 A box of 50 chocolate bars weighs 10 kg. How much does each chocolate bar weigh in grams?

17 A bar of soap weighs 0.2 kg. 120 g are used. How much soap is left?

18 A fish bowl contains 4.2 litres of water. 360 ml is spilt. How much water does the bowl hold now?

19 A sachet of shampoo contains 250 ml. There are twelve sachets in a box. How many litres of shampoo are there in the box?

20 A test tube holds 0.1 litres of a liquid. 38 ml is added. How much liquid is there in the test tube?

21 26 ml of cycle oil is used from a 200 ml can. A further 47 ml is used. How much oil is left?

22 How many 80 ml scoops of ice cream can be taken from a 2 litre tub?

On these pages you will write equations and solve equations.

Solve $4n + 3 = 11$	Solve $3n - 4 = 11$
$\boxed{4n} + 3 = 11$	$\boxed{3n} - 4 = 11$
$4n = 8$	$3n = 15$
$n = 2$	$n = 5$
because $4 \times \boxed{2} = 8$	because $3 \times \boxed{5} = 15$

Ⓜ

Solve the equations in Questions ① to ⑨ (find the value of n).

① $n + 3 = 7$ ④ $n - 2 = 18$ ⑦ $17 = 6 + n$

② $n + 11 = 31$ ⑤ $n - 4 = 24$ ⑧ $n + 4 = 4$

③ $n - 6 = 10$ ⑥ $16 = n + 3$ ⑨ $n - 8 = 12$

In Questions ⑩ to ⑮, copy and fill the empty boxes.

⑩ $\boxed{6n} + 7 = 19$ ⑫ $\boxed{8n} - 3 = 21$ ⑭ $\boxed{10n} + 6 = 46$

$\boxed{6n} = 12$ $\boxed{8n} = \square$ $\boxed{10n} = \square$

$n = \square$ $n = \square$ $n = \square$

⑪ $\boxed{5n} + 9 = 29$ ⑬ $\boxed{6n} - 8 = 34$ ⑮ $\boxed{9n} - 12 = 42$

$\boxed{5n} = \square$ $\boxed{6n} = \square$ $\boxed{9n} = \square$

$n = \square$ $n = \square$ $n = \square$

Solve the equations below:

⑯ $2n = 14$ ⑲ $8n + 6 = 22$ ㉒ $5n - 24 = 21$

⑰ $8n = 48$ ⑳ $10n + 7 = 67$ ㉓ $11 = 4n - 5$

⑱ $6n + 9 = 33$ ㉑ $3n - 11 = 16$ ㉔ $30 = 3n + 6$

Solve $5n + 1 = 2n + 10$

$\boxed{5n} + 1 = \boxed{2n} + 10$

$\boxed{3n} + 1 = 10$

$3n = 9$

$n = 3$

Solve $3n - 2 = n + 10$

$\boxed{3n} - 2 = \boxed{n} + 10$

$\boxed{2n} - 2 = 10$

$2n = 12$

$n = 6$

E

In Questions (1) to (6), copy and fill the empty boxes.

(1) $3n + 1 = n + 15$

$\boxed{2n} + 1 = 15$

$2n = \boxed{}$

$n = \boxed{}$

(4) $8n + 15 = 3n + 35$

$\boxed{} + 15 = 35$

$\boxed{} = 20$

$n = \boxed{}$

(2) $6n + 5 = 2n + 41$

$\boxed{} + 5 = 41$

$\boxed{} = 36$

$n = \boxed{}$

(5) $10n + 12 = 3n + 33$

$\boxed{} + 12 = 33$

$\boxed{} = \boxed{}$

$n = \boxed{}$

(3) $4n + 2 = n + 17$

$\boxed{} + 2 = 17$

$\boxed{} = 15$

$n = \boxed{}$

(6) $7n + 11 = 5n + 19$

$\boxed{} + 11 = 19$

$\boxed{} = \boxed{}$

$n = \boxed{}$

Solve the equations below:

(7) $7n + 6 = 3n + 22$

(8) $9n + 9 = 2n + 65$

(9) $5n + 12 = 3n + 40$

(10) $10n + 16 = 4n + 46$

(11) $7n + 11 = 2n + 46$

(12) $8n - 7 = 5n + 17$

(13) $4n - 10 = n + 50$

(14) $12n - 8 = 2n + 82$

On these pages you will find equations of straight lines, particularly lines which are parallel to the *x*-axis or *y*-axis.

Earlier in this book, we looked at vertical and horizontal lines.

- The points P, Q, R and S have coordinates (4, 4), (4, 3), (4, 2) and (4, 1) and they all lie on a straight line. Since the *x*-coordinate of all the points is 4, we say the *equation* of the line is $x = 4$.

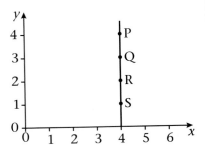

- The points A, B, C and D have coordinates (1, 3), (2, 3), (3, 3) and (4, 3) and they all lie on a straight line. Since the *y*-coordinate of all the points is 3, we say the *equation* of the line is $y = 3$.

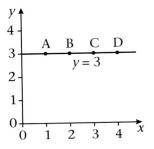

Ⓜ

①   Write down the equations of the lines marked A, B and C.

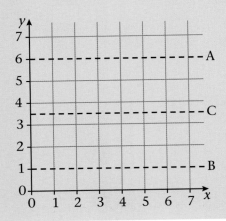

2 Write down the equations of the lines marked P, Q and R.

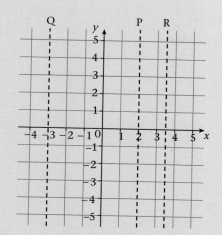

3 Copy the graph and then write down the coordinates for each point.

A (2, 1)   H (,)

B (,)   I (,)

C (,)   J (,)

D (,)   K (,)

E (,)   L (,)

F (,)   M (,)

G (,)   N (,)

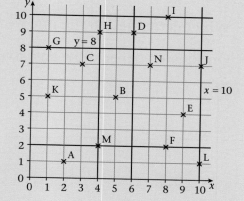

4 L lies on the line $x = 10$.
Which other letter lies on $x = 10$?

5 Which letter lies on $x = 6$?

6 Which letters lie on $x = 4$?

7 G lies on the line $y = 8$. Which letter lies on $y = 10$?

8 Which letters lie on $y = 2$?

9 Which letters lie on $y = 5$?

10 Which letters lie on $y = 7$?

11 Which letter lies on $x = 9$?

12 Point M lies on $x = 4$ *and* $y = 2$. What point lies on $x = 8$ and $y = 2$?

13 What point lies on $x = 2$ and $y = 1$?

14 What point lies on $x = 10$ and $y = 7$?

E

Negative co-ordinates

1 Copy the diagram and then write down the coordinates for each point.

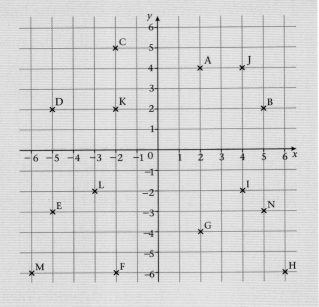

A (2,4)

B (5, 2)

C (–2, 5)

⋮

N(5, –3)

2 Point A lies on the line $x = 2$.
Which other letter lies on $x = 2$?

3 Point N lies on the line $y = –3$.
Which other letter lies on $y = –3$?

4 Which letters lie on the line $x = –5$?

5 Which letter lies on the line $y = 5$?

6 On squared paper, draw an x-axis from 0 to 7 and a y-axis from 0 to 7 like below.

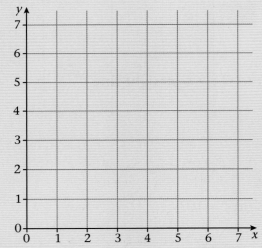

Put a cross at each of the following points:

(1, 1)   (4, 4)

(2, 2)   (5, 5)

(3, 3)   (6, 6)

Join up the crosses with a straight line.

The equation of the line is $y = x$ because for each point the y-coordinate is equal to the x-coordinate.

7 On squared paper, draw an x-axis from 0 to 7 and a y-axis from 0 to 7.
Put a cross at each of the following points:

(0, 5) (1, 4) (2, 3) (3, 2) (4, 1) (5, 0)

Join up the crosses with a straight line.

The equation of the line is $x + y = 5$ because the x-coordinate and the y-coordinate add up to 5.

On these pages you will practise drawing more straight line graphs.

Example

Draw the graph of $y = 2x$.

Answer

Pick 5 easy x-values: 0, 1, 2, 3, 4

Use $y = 2x$ to find y-values which belong to each x-value.

When $x = 0$, $y = 2x$ means $y = 2 \times x = 2 \times 0 = 0$

put in equation

so one point is $x = 0$, $y = 0$ (0, 0)

When $x = 1$, $y = 2x$ means $y = 2 \times 1 = 2$

so one point is $x = 1$, $y = 2$ (1, 2)

When $x = 2$, $y = 2 \times 2 = 4$ (2, 4)

When $x = 3$, $y = 2 \times 3 = 6$ (3, 6)

When $x = 4$, $y = 2 \times 4 = 8$ (4, 8)

Draw axes, plot the 5 points and join them up to make a straight line.

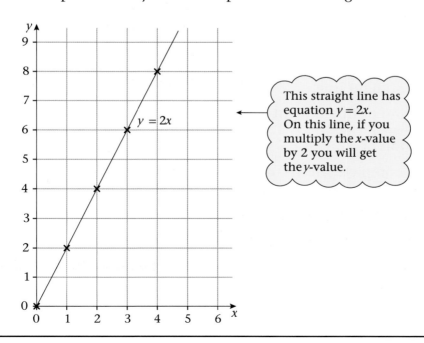

This straight line has equation $y = 2x$. On this line, if you multiply the x-value by 2 you will get the y-value.

Ⓜ

① The equation of a line is $y = 3x$.

Copy and complete this list of coordinates.

$x = 0, \quad y = 3x = 3 \times 0 = 0 \quad (0, 0)$

$x = 1, \quad y = 3 \times 1 = 3 \quad (1, 3)$

$x = 2, \quad y = \ldots = \boxed{} \quad (2, \boxed{})$

$x = 3, \quad y = \ldots = \boxed{} \quad (3, \boxed{})$

$x = 4, \quad y = \ldots = \boxed{} \quad (4, \boxed{})$

Draw these axes on squared paper.

Plot the 5 points above.

Join up the points to make a straight line.

The equation of this line is $y = 3x$.

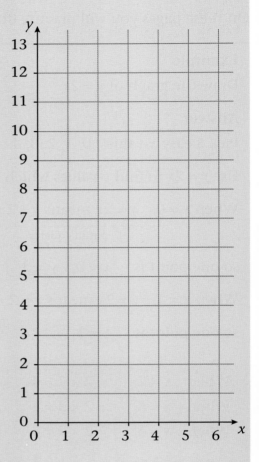

② The equation of a line is $y = x + 4$.

Copy and complete this list of co-ordinates.

$x = 0, \quad y = 0 + 4 = 4 \quad (0, 4)$

$x = 1, \quad y = 1 + 4 = 5 \quad (1, 5)$

$x = 2, \quad y = \ldots = \boxed{} \quad (2, \boxed{})$

$x = 3, \quad y = \ldots = \boxed{} \quad (3, \boxed{})$

$x = 4, \quad y = \ldots = \boxed{} \quad (4, \boxed{})$

On squared paper, draw an x-axis from 0 to 6

and a y-axis from 0 to 9 like below:

Plot the 5 points from above. Join up these points

to make a straight line.

The equation of this straight line is $y = x + 4$.

③ The equation of a line is $y = 5x$.

Copy and complete this list of co-ordinates.

$x = 0, \qquad y = 5 \times 0 = 0 \quad (0, 0)$

$\qquad\qquad\qquad\qquad\quad (1, 5)$

$\qquad\qquad\qquad\qquad\quad (2, \boxed{})$

$\qquad\qquad\qquad\qquad\quad (3, \boxed{})$

$\qquad\qquad\qquad\qquad\quad (4, \boxed{})$

On squared paper, draw an x-axis from 0 to 6 and a y-axis from 0 to 20.

Plot the 5 points from above. Join up the points to make a straight line.

E

For each Question below you will need to draw axes like these:

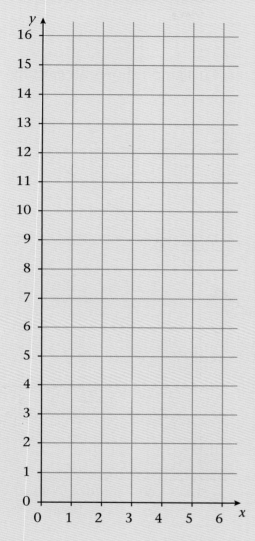

1 $y = 7 - x$

Complete the co-ordinates:

$(0, 7)$ $(1, 6)$ $(2, \square)$ $(3, \square)$ $(4, \square)$

Plot these points and draw the graph.

2 $y = 2x + 3$

Complete the co-ordinates.

$(0, 3)$ $(1, 5)$ $(2, \square)$ $(3, \square)$ $(4, \square)$

Plot these points and draw the graph.

3 $y = 3x + 1$

Complete the co-ordinates.

$(0, 1)$ $(1, 4)$ $(2, \square)$ $(3, \square)$ $(4, \square)$

Plot these points and draw the graph.

4 $y = 2x - 2$

Complete the co-ordinates.

$(1, 0)$ $(2, 2)$ $(3, \square)$ $(4, \square)$ $(5, \square)$

Draw the graph.

5 $y = 4x - 1$

Complete the co-ordinates.

$(1, 3)$ $(2, 7)$ $(3, \square)$ $(4, \square)$

Draw the graph.

6 $y = 3x - 3$

Complete the co-ordinates.

$(1, 0)$ $(2, \square)$ $(3, \square)$ $(4, \square)$ $(5, \square)$

Draw the graph.

Note

Check all your graphs with a computer or graphical calculator if possible.

On these pages you will read from graphs and draw graphs from real-life events.

M

1) A man earns £40 a day picking fruit for 10 hours. This graph shows his earnings for 80 hours (8 days).

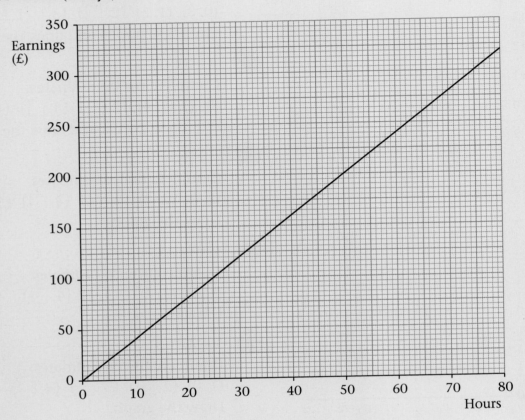

a) What does one small square show you on the vertical axis?

b) What does one small square show you on the horizontal axis?

c) How much does the man earn in 2 days (20 hours)?

d) How much does the man earn in 5 days (50 hours)?

e) How much does the man earn in 7 days (70 hours)?

f) How much does the man earn in 4½ days (45 hours)?

g) How many HOURS must he work to earn £100?

h) How many HOURS must he work to earn £60?

i) How many DAYS must he work to earn £200?

j) How many DAYS must he work to earn £160?

k) How many DAYS must he work to earn £320?

1 Find the largest share in these problems
a) £64, ratio 3:5
b) 90 kg, ratio 7:2
c) 220 m, ratio 3:3:4

2 Find the smallest share in these problems
a) £72, ratio 1:11
b) 66 cm, ratio 2:1
c) 35 litres, ratio 2:3:2

3 Alan and Ben share some money in the ratio 3:5.
Alan gets £30. How much does Ben get?

4 A box of chocolates has hard and soft centres in the ratio 2:5.
If there are 20 soft ones in the box, how many hard ones are there?

5 The ratio of red pens to blue pens in a box is 1:4.
If there are 40 blue pens how many red ones are there?

6 A class contains boys and girls in the ratio 4:3.
If there are 16 boys in the class, how many girls are there?

7 A shop sells biscuits and cakes in the ratio 3:2.
If it sells 300 biscuits, how many cakes will it sell?

8 A paper-shop sells the Sun and the Mirror in the ratio 7:2.
If it sells 40 copies of the Mirror, how many copies of the Sun does it sell?

9 A train carries men, women and children in the ratio 5:4:3.
If there are 80 women on the train.
a) how many children are there?
b) how many passengers are on the train altogether?

On these pages you will find the value of one item to help you find the value of several items.

> **Example**
> If 10 CDs cost £150, how much will 7 CDs cost?
> FIND THE COST OF *ONE* CD.
> 1 CD costs £150 ÷ 10 = £15.
> so 7 CDs cost £15 × 7 = £105.

M

1. If 4 pencils cost 80p, find the cost of 9 pencils.
2. If 7 rulers cost £2:10, find the cost of 3 rulers.
3. If 6 shirts cost £90, find the cost of 8 shirts.
4. If 5 bars of chocolate cost 95p, how much will 2 bars of chocolate cost?
5. If 7 identical children weigh 350 kg, find the total weight of 4 identical children.
6. Five CDs cost £60. How much will 8 CDs cost?
7. Seven doughnuts cost 84p. How much will you pay for 10 doughnuts?
8. Six wooden chairs cost £120. How much will 15 chairs cost?
9. Eight pizzas cost £32. How much will 5 pizzas cost?
10. Twelve bottles of wine cost £60. How much will 5 bottles cost?
11. Fifteen rugby shirts cost £300. How much will you pay for 9 shirts?
12. If 7 bakers make 126 loaves in an hour. How many loaves would 9 bakers make in one hour?

E

1. If 5 hammers cost £20, find the cost of 7.
2. Magazines cost £16 for 8. Find the cost of 3 magazines.
3. Find the cost of 2 cakes if 7 cakes cost £10.50.
4. A machine fills 1000 bottles in 5 minutes. How many bottles will it fill in 2 minutes?
5. There are 528 cars in a 3 mile traffic jam. About how many cars are there in an 8 mile jam?

6 A train travels 100 km in 20 minutes. How long will it take to travel 50 km?

7 11 discs cost £13.20. Find the cost of 4 discs.

8 If 7 cartons of milk hold 14 litres, find how much milk there is in 6 cartons.

9 A worker takes 8 minutes to make 2 circuit boards. How long would it take to make 7 circuit boards?

10 The total weight of 8 tiles is 1720 g. How much do 17 tiles weigh?

11 A machine can fill 3000 bottles in 15 minutes. How many bottles will it fill in 2 minutes?

12 A witch travels 40 km in 120 minutes. How long will she take to travel 55 km at the same speed?

13 If 4 grapefruit can be bought for £2.96, how many can be bought for £8.14?

14 £15 can be exchanged for 126 francs. How many francs can be exchanged for £37.50?

15

N&E STORE	
5 pieces of timber	£21
20 screws	£1.50
50 nails	£1.20
3 m felt	£4.80

Nick is building a garden shed. He has two plans which he could use. What he needs for each plan is shown below. Using the prices from the N&E Store, use a calculator to find out which is the cheaper plan and by how much?

Plan A

7m felt
100 screws
200 nails
12 pieces of timber

Plan B

120 screws
11 pieces of timber
10m felt
175 nails

On these pages you will learn to visualise 3-D shapes from 2-D drawings.

Ⓜ

a) Without using cubes, work out how many cubes are needed to build these shapes.

b) Use cubes to build these shapes.

c) How many more cubes are needed to make each shape into a cuboid?

Examples

① a) 6 cubes are needed to build this shape.

  b) 3 more cubes are needed to make it into a cuboid.

② a) 6 cubes are needed to build this shape.

  b) 6 more cubes are needed to make it into a cuboid.

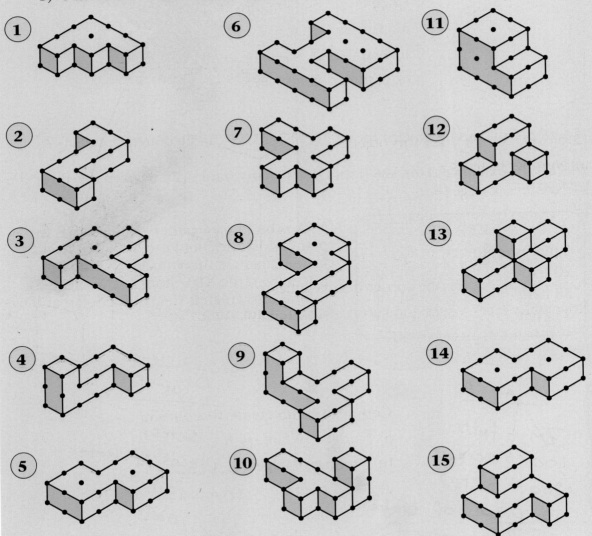

Faces, edges and vertices

Many three-dimensional shapes have *faces*, *edges* and *vertices* (plural of *vertex*). The diagram opposite shows a cuboid.

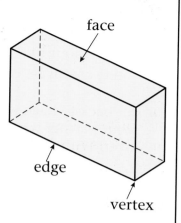

The *faces* of the cuboid are the flat surfaces on the shape.

There are 6 faces on a cuboid.

The *edges* of the cuboid are the lines that make up the shape.

There are 12 edges on a cuboid.

The vertices of the cuboid are where the edges meet at a point.

There are 8 vertices on a cuboid.

E

1

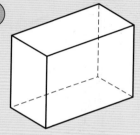

Copy and complete for this object:

a) Number of faces = _____

b) Number of edges = _____

c) Number of vertices = _____

2 Copy and complete for this object:

a) Number of faces = _____

b) Number of edges = _____

c) Number of vertices = _____

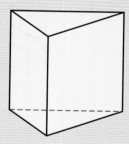

3 Suppose you cut off one corner from a cube.

How many faces, edges and vertices has the remaining shape?

How about the piece cut off?

4

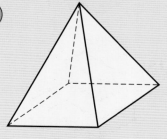

Copy and complete for this object:

a) Number of faces = _____

b) Number of edges = _____

c) Number of vertices = _____

5 Draw 3 pictures of a cube and label them A, B, C.

On A colour in a pair of edges which are parallel.

On B colour in a pair of edges which are perpendicular.

On C colour in a pair of edges which are neither parallel nor intersect each other.

6 Sit back to back with a partner. Look at one of the models below but don't tell your partner which one. Tell your partner how to make the model. Now swap over. With practice you can design harder models of your own.

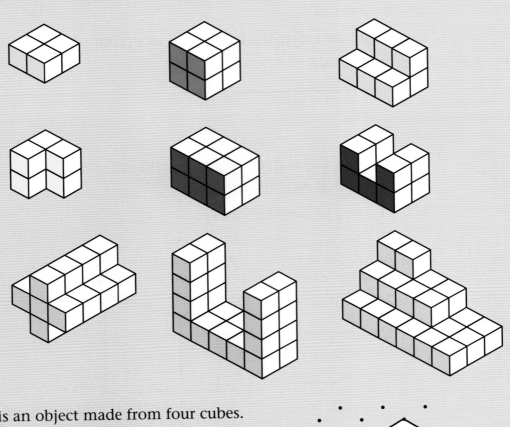

7 Here is an object made from four cubes.

a) Copy the drawing on isometric paper. (Make sure you have the paper the right way round.)

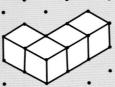

b) Make as many *different* objects as you can using four cubes. Draw each object on isometric paper.

On these pages you will learn to make 3-D objects.

- If the cube shown was made of cardboard, and you cut along some of the edges and laid it out flat, you would have a *net* of the cube.
  There is more than one net of a cube as you will see in the exercise below.

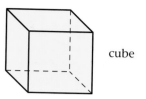

cube

- To make a cube from card you need to produce the net shown below complete with the added 'tabs' for glueing purposes.

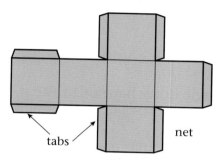

tabs   net

- In this section you will make several interesting 3D objects. You will need a pencil, ruler, scissors, and either glue (Pritt Stick) or Sellotape.

M

(1) Here are several nets which may or may not make cubes. Draw the nets on squared paper, cut them out and fold them to see which ones do make cubes.

a)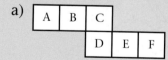

c)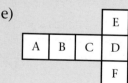

e)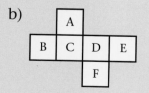

b)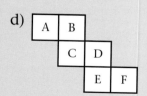

d)

(2) For the nets, which *did* make cubes in Question (1), state which of the faces B, C, D, E or F was opposite face A on the cube.

204

3 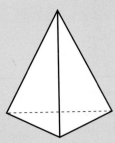 This is a *tetrahedron* (a triangular pyramid)

Which of these nets will make a tetrahedron?

a) 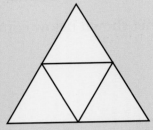   b) 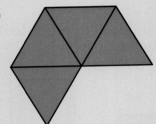   c)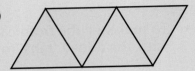

4 Copy the nets onto triangle dotty paper. Cut them out and see if you were right.

5 Use triangle dotty paper again.
Can you make a net for a triangular based prism?

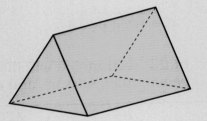

6 Use triangle dotty paper. Draw the net below and make this solid (called an octahedron).

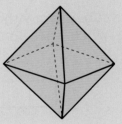   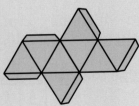

Ask your teacher for cardboard.

1 Use a ruler and protractor to draw this triangle in the middle of the cardboard. All lengths are in cm.

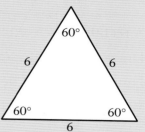

2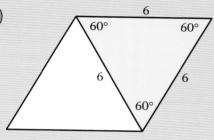

Use a ruler and protractor to draw this triangle joined to the first triangle.

3 Use a ruler and protractor to draw 2 more triangles joined to your first triangle.

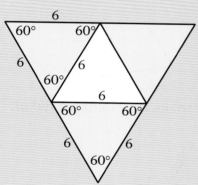

4 Draw on some flaps like this:

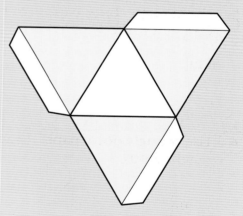

5 Cut out, fold and glue to make a tetrahedron.

6 Draw a net for a cuboid which has length = 5 cm, width = 3 cm and height = 2 cm.

7 Use triangle dotty paper. Draw the net below and make this solid (called an icosahedron).

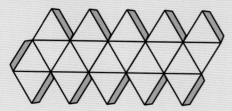 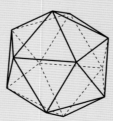

Scale Drawings

On these pages you will learn to use scale drawings.

A rectangle has length 12 m and width 9 m.

Draw an accurate scale drawing of the rectangle using a scale of 1 cm for every 4 m.

Length 12 m will be 12 ÷ 4 = 3 cm on the drawing.

Width 8 m will be 8 ÷ 4 = 2 cm on the drawing.

3 cm

Scale drawing: 2 cm

Ⓜ

Draw an accurate scale drawing of each shape below using the scale shown.

(1)   12 m

6 m   Use 1 cm for every 3 m.

(2)   20 m

25 m   Use 1 cm for every 5 m.

(3) Use 1 cm for every 10 m.

Measure and write down the length of AB (in cm).

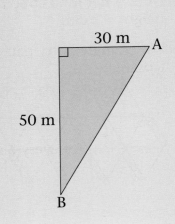

30 m   A

50 m

B

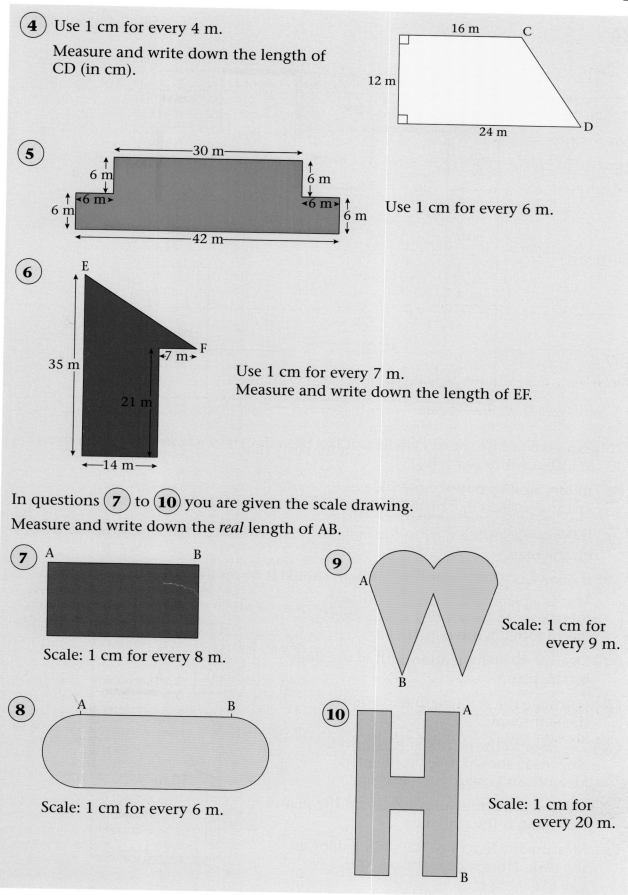

4 Use 1 cm for every 4 m.

Measure and write down the length of CD (in cm).

16 m
C
12 m
24 m
D

5
30 m
6 m
6 m
6 m
6 m
6 m
6 m
6 m
42 m

Use 1 cm for every 6 m.

6
E
35 m
7 m
F
21 m
14 m

Use 1 cm for every 7 m.
Measure and write down the length of EF.

In questions **7** to **10** you are given the scale drawing.
Measure and write down the *real* length of AB.

7 A   B

Scale: 1 cm for every 8 m.

9
A
B

Scale: 1 cm for every 9 m.

8 A   B

Scale: 1 cm for every 6 m.

10
A
B

Scale: 1 cm for every 20 m.

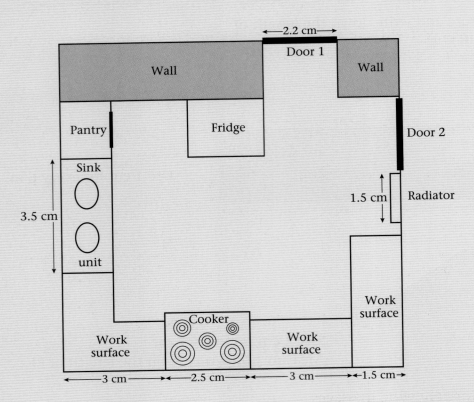

This is a plan of Mrs Smith's kitchen. It has been drawn to a scale of 1 cm for every 40 cm (often written as 1:40).

1 In Mrs Smith's house, how wide is
   a) the cooker   b) the sink unit   c) the radiator   d) door 1?

2 If the work surface next to the radiator is 160 cm long what length would it be on the plan?

3 If door 2 is 92 cm wide, what length should it be on the plan?

This is a plan of Mr Hazel's bathroom.
It is drawn to a scale of 1 cm for every
50 cm (often written as 1:50).

4 Measure the length and width of the floor on the plan.

5 Calculate the real length and width of the bathroom.

6 The door to the bedroom is 1 m wide. How wide should it be on the plan? Measure and check your answer.

7 The towel rail measures 1.8 cm on the plan. How long is the real one?

8 Measure the length of the sliding door on the plan. How wide is the real one?

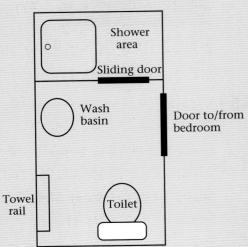

On these pages you will plot co-ordinates with negative numbers and find the co-ordinates of the midpoints of lines.

The letters from A to Z are shown on the grid.

Coded messages can be sent using coordinates.

For example (–4, –2) (–4, 2) (–4, 2) (4, 2) reads 'FOOD'.

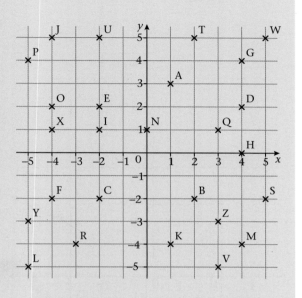

Decipher the following messages

1 (5, 5) (4, 0) (1, 3) (2, 5) # (4, 2) (–4, 2) # (–5, –3)
(–4, 2) (–2, 5) # (–2, –2) (1, 3) (–5, –5) (–5, –5) #
(1, 3) # (4, –4) (1, 3) (0, 1) # (5, 5) (–2, 1) (2, 5) (4, 0) #
(1, 3) # (5, –2) (–5, 4) (1, 3) (4, 2) (–2, 2) # (–2, 1)
(0, 1) # (4, 0) (–2, 1) (5, –2) # (4, 0) (–2, 2) (1, 3)
(4, 2) ? # (4, 2) (–4, 2) (–2, 5) (4, 4) !

2 (5, 5) (4, 0) (1, 3) (2, 5) # (4, 2) (–4, 2) # (–5, –3)
(–4, 2) (–2, 5) # (–2, –2) (1, 3) (–5, –5) (–5, –5) #
(1, 3) # (4, 2) (–2, 2) (1, 3) (4, 2) # (–5, 4) (1, 3) (–3, –4)
(–3, –4) (–4, 2) (2, 5) ? # (–5, 4) (–4, 2) (–5, –5) (–5, –3)
(4, 4) (–4, 2) (0, 1) !

3 (5, 5) (–2, 1) (2, 5) (4, 0) # (5, 5) (4, 0) (1, 3) (2, 5) #
(4, 2) (–4, 2) # (–5, –3) (–4, 2) (–2, 5) # (5, –2) (2, 5)
(–2, 5) (–4, –2) (–4, –2) # (1, 3) # (4, 2) (–2, 2) (1, 3)
(4, 2) # (–5, 4) (1, 3) (–3, –4) (–3, –4) (–4, 2)
(2, 5) ? # (–5, 4) (–4, 2) (–5, –5) (–5, –3) (–4, –2) (–2, 1)
(–5, –5) (–5, –5) (1, 3) !

4 Write a message or joke of your own using coordinates. Ask a friend to decipher your words.

Example

Two sides of a rectangle are drawn.

Find the co-ordinates of the fourth vertex (corner) of the rectangle.

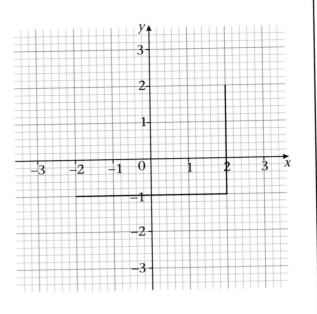

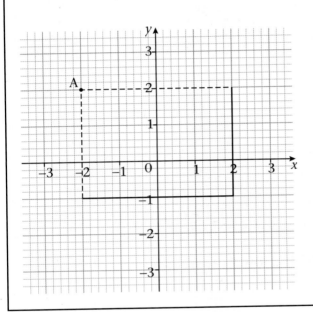

The fourth vertex (corner) of the rectangle is at A

i.e. (–2, 2)

E

1 Copy the graph shown.

A, B and C are three corners of a square. Draw the square and write down the co-ordinates of the other vertex (corner).

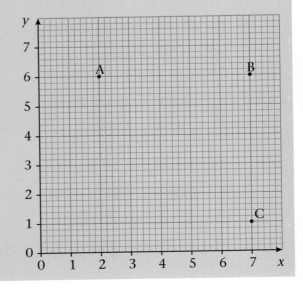

2 Copy the grid.

Plot each set of co-ordinates below in the order given to form two sides of a rectangle.

Complete the rectangle and write down the co-ordinate of the missing vertex.

a) (1, 4) (1, −4) (−3, −4) (,)

b) (1, 2) (1, 5) (4, 5) (,)

c) (−2, 3) (4, 3) (4, −2) (,)

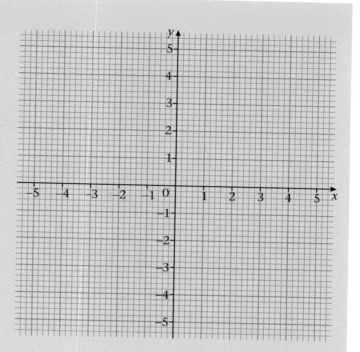

3 Copy the same grid used in Question **2**.

a) Plot the points (−2, 1) (−2, 3) and (−1, 1). Join them up to make a triangle.

b) *Translate* the triangle 3 units parallel to the x-axis. Write down the co-ordinates of the 3 vertices (corners) of the new triangle.

c) *Reflect* the first triangle in the x-axis. Write down the co-ordinates of the 3 vertices (corners) of the new triangle.

4 Copy the same grid used in Question **2**.

a) Plot the points (0, 2) (−1, 2) (−2, 1) (−2, 0) (−1, −1) and (0, −1). Join these points in the order shown above.

b) Reflect this shape in the y-axis.

c) What is the name of the whole shape that is now drawn?

5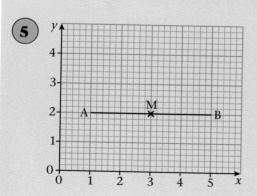

M is the midpoint (middle) of line AB. Write down the co-ordinates of M.

212

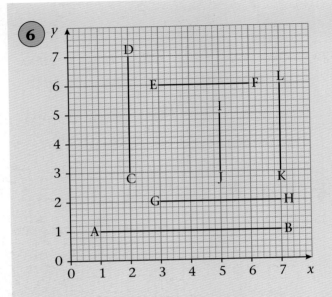

6

Write down the co-ordinates of the midpoint of the line:

a) AB   d) GH
b) CD   e) IJ
c) EF   f) KL

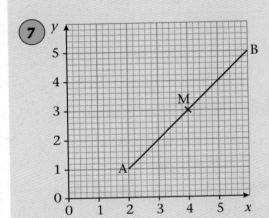

7

M is the midpoint (middle) of line AB.
Write down the co-ordinates of M.

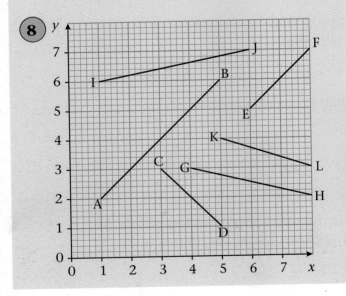

8

Write down the co-ordinates of the midpoint of the line:

a) AB   d) GH
b) CD   e) IJ
c) EF   f) KL

Constructing Triangles 2

On these pages you will draw accurate triangles when you know 2 sides and an angle or 2 angles and a side or 3 sides only.

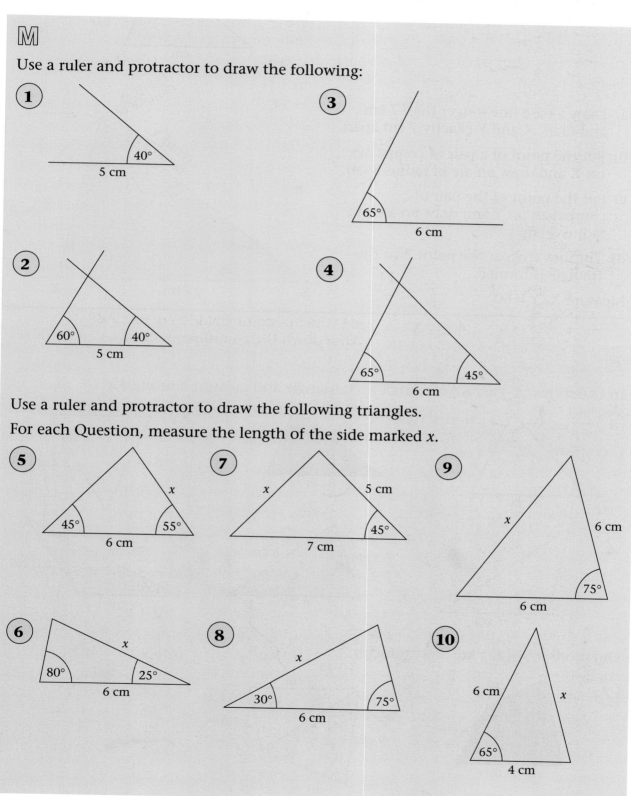

Ⓜ

Use a ruler and protractor to draw the following:

① 40° 5 cm

③ 65° 6 cm

② 60° 40° 5 cm

④ 65° 45° 6 cm

Use a ruler and protractor to draw the following triangles.

For each Question, measure the length of the side marked *x*.

⑤ 45° 55° *x* 6 cm

⑦ *x* 5 cm 45° 7 cm

⑨ *x* 6 cm 75° 6 cm

⑥ 80° *x* 25° 6 cm

⑧ *x* 30° 75° 6 cm

⑩ 6 cm *x* 65° 4 cm

Constructing a triangle given three sides

Draw triangle XYZ and measure XẐY.

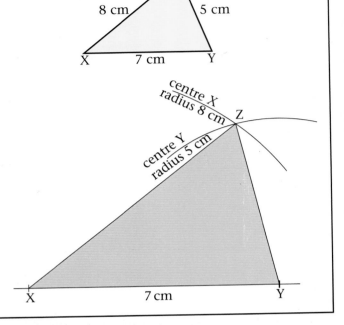

a) Draw a base line longer than 7 cm and mark X and Y exactly 7 cm apart.

b) Put the point of a pair of compasses on X and draw an arc of radius 8 cm.

c) Put the point of the pair of compasses on Y and draw an arc of radius 5 cm.

d) The arcs cross at the point Z so the triangle is formed.

Measure XẐY = 60°

E

In Questions ① to ⑥ construct each triangle and measure the angle x.

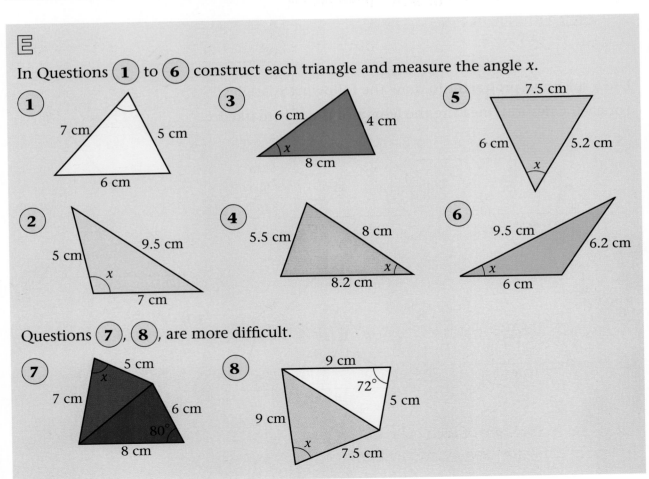

Questions ⑦, ⑧, are more difficult.

On these pages you will find the surface area and volume of different cuboids.

Example

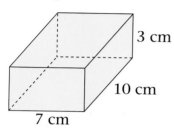

Volume = length × width × height
Volume = 10 × 7 × 3
       = 70 × 3
       = 210 cm³

There are 6 faces.
Front face area = 7 × 3 = 21
Back face area = 7 × 3 = 21
Top face area = 10 × 7 = 70

Bottom face area = 10 × 7 = 70
Side 1 face area = 10 × 3 = 30
Side 2 face area = 10 × 3 = 30
Total surface area = 242 cm²

Ⓜ

1 Find the surface area of each cuboid below:
All lengths are in cm.

a)

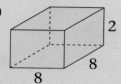

d)

g)

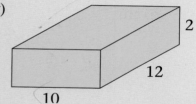

b)

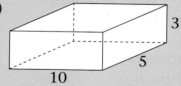

e)

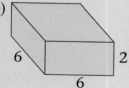

h)

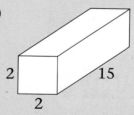

c)

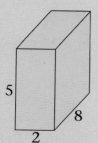

f)

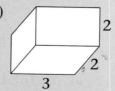

i)

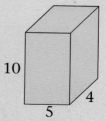

2 Find the volume of each cuboid in Question **1**.
(The units for each answer will be cm³.)

E

You may use a calculator for the following Questions.

1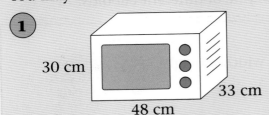

30 cm

48 cm

33 cm

A microwave oven has a height of 30 cm, a width of 48 cm and a depth of 33 cm. Calculate

a) its volume

b) the area of the top.

2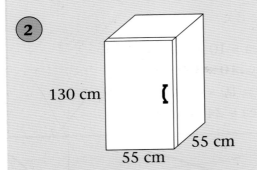

130 cm

55 cm

55 cm

A fridge is 130 cm high and its length and width are both 55 cm. Calculate

a) the area of its door

b) its volume.

3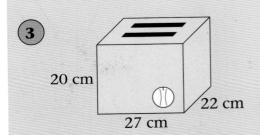

20 cm

27 cm

22 cm

A pop-up toaster is 27 cm wide, 22 cm long and is 20 cm high. Calculate

a) the area of its 4 sides

b) its volume.

4

A box of breakfast cereal measures 6 cm × 10 cm × 16 cm. Calculate

a) the total surface area of the box

b) the volume of the box.

5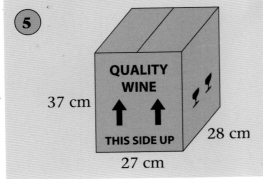

QUALITY WINE

THIS SIDE UP

37 cm

28 cm

27 cm

A box of wine measures 37 cm × 27 cm × 28 cm. Calculate

a) the total surface area of the box

b) the volume of the box.

On these pages you will construct frequency tables and use frequency diagrams.

Example

- Here are the ages of the people at a wedding.

  33 11 45 22 50 38 23 54 18 72 5 58
  37 3 61 51 7 62 24 57 31 27 66 29
  25 39 48 15 52 25 35 18 49 63 13 74

  With so many different numbers over a wide range it is
  helpful to put the ages into *groups*.

- Here is the start of a tally chart

Ages	Tally	Total (Frequency)
0–9	|||	3
10–19	⅄ℋ	5
20–29	⅄ℋ ||	7
30–39		
40–49		
50–59		
60–69		
70–79		

- Here is the start of a frequency chart

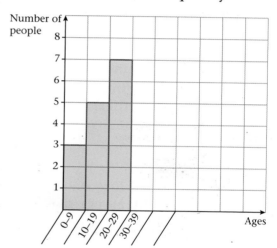

- Finish the tally chart and the frequency
  diagram.

  Notice that when the data is in groups
  the bars are touching.

(1) Shruti started with one frog but it laid eggs and now
she has lots! One day she measures all her little pets.
Here are the lengths in mm.

82 63 91 78 27 93 87 48 22 15
42 28 84 65 87 55 79 66 85 38

(a) Make a tally chart and then draw the frequency diagram.

Length (mm)	Tally	Frequency
0–20		
21–40		
41–60		
61–80		
81–100		

(b) How many frogs were more than 60 mm long?

2 Tom has lots of snakes and he likes to weigh them every week. The weights are shown.

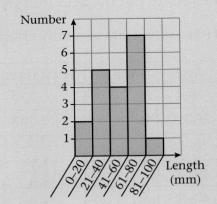

(a) How many snakes weigh between 61 and 80 grams?

(b) How many snakes weigh less than 41 grams?

(c) How many snakes does he have altogether?

3 Eggs are sorted into size by weight. The weight is then converted into an egg size. The sizes range from 1 to 7.

Here are the weights of eggs produced by a farmer's chickens.

65, 56, 62, 69, 64, 51, 53, 57, 60, 59,
45, 59, 50, 57, 54, 58, 53, 59, 55, 58,
56, 46, 55, 44, 61, 55, 52, 70, 60, 56,
70, 66, 62, 42, 49, 63, 50, 57, 64, 72.

Copy and complete this table:

Weight (grams)	Size	Tally	Frequency
Under 45 g	7		
45–49	6		
50–54	5		
55–59	4		
60–64	3		
65–69	2		
70 g or over	1		

1 Here are the heights of the 21 members of a school swimming team

136.8, 146.2, 141.2, 147.2, 151.3, 145.0, 155.0,

149.9, 138.0, 146.8, 157.4, 143.1, 143.5, 147.2,

147.5, 158.6, 154.7, 144.6, 152.4, 144.0, 151.0.

(a) Put the heights into groups

class interval	frequency
$135 \leq h < 140$	
$140 \leq h < 145$	
$145 \leq h < 150$	

(b) Draw a frequency diagram

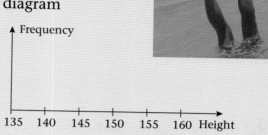

2 A group of 7 year-olds were each accompanied by one of their parents on a coach trip to a zoo. Each person on the coach was weighed in kg. Here are the weights:

21.1, 45.7, 22.3, 26.3, 50.1, 24.3, 44.2,

54.3, 53.2, 46.0, 51.0, 24.2, 56.4, 20.6,

25.5, 22.8, 52.0, 26.5, 41.8, 27.5, 29.7,

55.1, 30.7, 47.4, 23.5, 59.8, 49.3, 23.4,

21.7, 57.6, 22.6, 58.7, 28.6, 54.1.

(a) Put the weights into groups.

class interval	frequency
$20 \leq w < 25$	
$25 \leq w < 30$	
$30 \leq w < 35$	
$\vdots$	

(b) Draw a frequency diagram.

3 Farmer Gray rears pigs. As an experiment, he decided to feed half of his pigs with their normal diet and the other half on a new high fibre diet. The diagrams shows the weight of the pigs in the two groups.

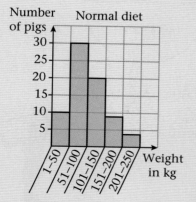

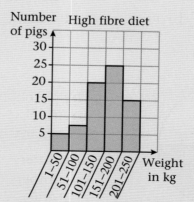

In one sentence describe what effect the new diet had.

On these pages you will learn to interpret and draw pie charts.

Examples

The favourite colours of 80 children.

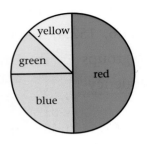

Colour	Children
red	40
blue	20
green	10
yellow	10

The 300 members of the audience at a performance of Toy Story.

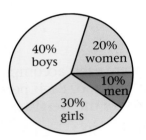

Group	Number
boys	120
girls	90
women	60
men	30

Ⓜ

①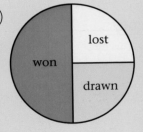

The pie chart shows the results of the 20 games played by a school football team. How many games were:

a) won   b) lost   c) drawn?

② The pie chart shows the 50 passengers travelling on a bus.
How many of the passengers were:

a) women   b) men   c) children?

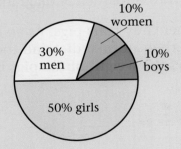

③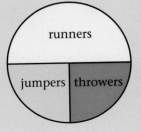

The pie chart shows the 60 competitors at an Athletics Meeting.
How many of the competitors were:

a) runners
b) jumpers
c) throwers?

4 The pie chart shows the 48 votes for the Year 8 candidates for the School Council. How many votes did each candidate receive?

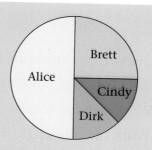

5

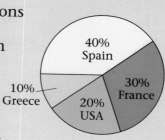

The pie chart shows the numbers of passengers in 200 cars. Copy and complete the table.

Passengers	Cars
0	
1	
2	
3	
3+	

6 The pie chart shows the holiday destinations of 400 tourists waiting for their flights. How many tourists were travelling to each country?

Example

A survey about eye colour was done. The results are below:

Eye colour	frequency (number of people)
blue	25
brown	20
green	10
grey	5

Draw a pie chart to show this information.

Method

a) Add all the numbers:
   25 + 20 + 10 + 5 = 60 people.

b) Whole angle in a pie chart = 360°
   The must be split between 60 people.
   Angle for each person = 360° ÷ 60
   = 6°

c) Angle for 'blue' = 25 × 6° = 150°
   Angle for 'brown' = 20 × 6° = 120°
   Angle for 'green' = 10 × 6° = 60°
   Angle for 'grey' = 5 × 6° = 30°

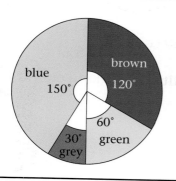

E

1 A 'Chewit' bar contains these four ingredients:

    Oats 6 g   Barley 9 g   Sugar 3 g   Rye 18 g

a) Work out the total weight of the ingredients.

b) Work out the angle on a pie chart for 1 g of the ingredients
[i.e. 360° ÷ (total weight)].

c) Work out the angle for each ingredient and draw a pie chart.

In Questions **2** to **4**, work out the angle for each item and draw a pie chart.

2 Most popular countries for Holidays

Country	Frequency
Spain	11
France	17
Greece	6
Italy	8
USA	3

3 Pupil's favourite colour.

Colour	Frequency
red	41
yellow	52
blue	24
green	30
pink	13
gold	20

4 Most popular car model.

Model	Frequency
Nissan	2
Ford	5
Fiat	2
Jaguar	6
Mitsubishi	3

5 At the 'Crooked Corkscrew' last Friday,
120 customers ordered meals.

    40 ordered beefburger

    20 ordered ham salad

    16 ordered curry

    25 ordered snake

    19 ordered snake with egg.

Draw a pie chart to show this information.

6 Eurostar did a survey of over a thousand passengers on one of their trains.
Here are their nationalities:

    British 30%   French 20%   German 15%   Dutch 35%

On a pie chart, the angle for British passengers is found by working out 30% of
360°. Find the angle on a pie chart representing

(a) French passengers   (b) Dutch passengers.

On these pages you will find things out from different charts and compare 2 sets of data.

M

1)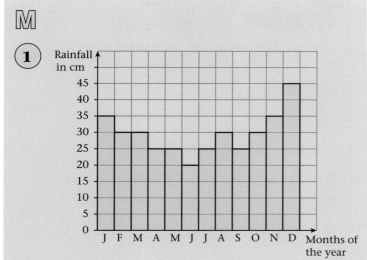

The monthly rainfall in the Lake District is shown left.

a) How much rain fell in August?

b) Which was the driest month in the year?

c) Which was the wettest month in the year?

d) In which months did 25 cm of rain fall?

e) In which months did 30 cm of rain fall?

2) The bar charts show the sale of different things over a year but the labels on the charts have been lost. Decide which of the charts A, B, C or D shows sales of:

a) Christmas trees

b) Crisps

c) Flower seeds

d) Greetings cards [including Christmas, Valentine's Day, etc.]

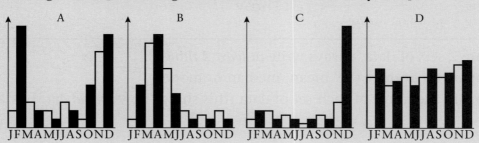

3) Here is some information about fireworks.

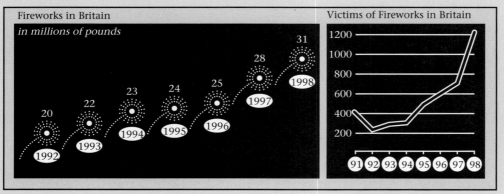

In which year was the lowest number of people injured by fireworks?

5 The bar chart shows the spectators attending various sporting fixtures.

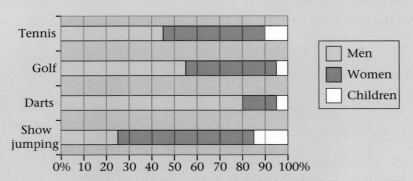

a) What percentage of the spectators at the golf were men?

b) What percentage of the spectators at the tennis were children?

c) What percentage of the spectators at the show jumping were women?

d) What percentage of the spectators at the darts were not men?

6 Here is an age distribution pyramid for the children at a Center Parcs resort.

(a) How many girls were there aged 5–9?

(b) How many children were there altogether in the 0–4 age range?

(c) How many girls were at the resort?

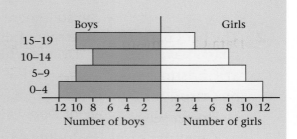

To compare 2 sets of data, always write *at least 2 things*:

(1)   Compare an average (i.e. mean, median or mode)

(2)   Compare the range of each set of data (this shows how *spread out* the data is)

Example

Data A: 1 2 3 4 5

Data B: 3 3 3 3 3

For Data A: find an average, e.g. median = 3
              find the range, i.e. 5 – 1 = 4

For Data B: find an average, e.g. median = 3
              find the range, i.e. 3 – 3 = 0

Compare Data A and Data B.

Answer

The median for Data A is the same as the median for Data B but the range of Data A is greater than the range of Data B (i.e. Data A is more spread out).

E

1 Data A: 2 3 7 8 9

Data B: 2 3 4 5 6

Copy and complete the statements below to compare Data A and Data B:

Data A: median = _____   range = _____

Data B: median = _____   range = _____

'The median for Data A is (greater/smaller) than the median for Data B and the range of Data A is (greater/smaller) than the range of Data B (i.e. Data A is (more/less) spread out).'

2 Data C: 6 8 4 13 9 2

Data D: 12 5 14 11 4 8

Copy and complete the statements below to compare Data C and Data D:

Data C: mean = _____   range = _____

Data D: mean = _____   range = _____

'The mean for Data C is...........than the mean for Data D but the range of Data C is.........than the range of Data D (i.e. Data C is ....spread out).'

3 Some children in Year 8 were asked how many portions of fruit and vegetables they ate each day. The following were recorded:

Class 8C: mean = 2.3   range = 7

Class 8D: mean = 2.1   range = 6

Copy and complete the sentence below to compare portions eaten by children in class 8C and class 8D:

'The mean portion for class 8C is ....than the mean portions for class 8D and the range of portions for class 8C is .... than the range of portions for class 8D.'

4 Some pupils in Year 7 were asked how long it took them to walk to school. The following were recorded:

Class 7F: mean = 21 minutes   range = 49 minutes

Class 7H: mean = 24 minutes   range = 43 minutes

Write a sentence to compare the time taken to walk to school by pupils in class 7G and class 7H.

5 12 pupils in Year 7 and 12 pupils in Year 11 were asked how many hours of fishing they did each weekend. The results are recorded below:

Year 7   6 7 4 4 2 6 4 5 7 1 3 3

Year 11   2 1 1 5 3 5 6 8 4 3 1 2

a) Work out the median and range for Year 7.

b) Work out the median and range for Year 11.

c) Write a sentence to compare the number of hours of fishing by pupils in Year 7 and Year 11.

6 20 children were asked how many baths or showers they had each week (10 children from Year 8 and 10 children from Year 9). The results are below.

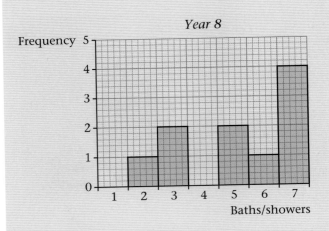

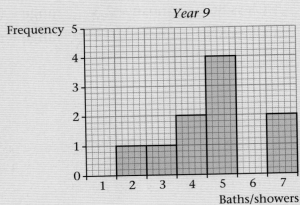

a) Work out the mean and range for Year 8.

b) Work out the mean and range for Year 9.

c) Write a sentence to compare the number of baths or showers taken by children in Year 8 and Year 9.

On these pages you will state a hypothesis, collect data, process data and interpret the data.

Task

1 Write down a hypothesis about heights of pupils in your class.
(**Example.** Girls are taller than boys.)
Show this to your teacher.

2 Discuss with your teacher how you can collect data to test your hypothesis.
Collect this data and record it.

3 Draw a chart to show your data. Discuss this with your teacher.
A possible chart is shown below:

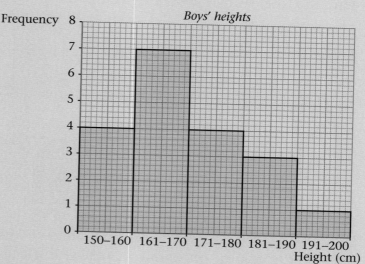

4 Copy and complete the table below (you may use a calculator).

	Median	Mean	Range
Boys			
Girls			

Check with your teacher.

5 Compare the boy's heights and the girls' heights (i.e. say something about the *median* or *mode* and say something about the *range*).

By looking at this and the chart(s), was your hypothesis true or false?

Use a computer to do the Data Handling Project in Section M.

In particular, try different charts (discuss with your teacher).

Find averages on the computer (discuss with your teacher).

1 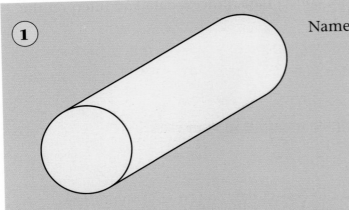 Name this solid.

2 Find the total surface area of this cuboid.

(Answer in cm²)

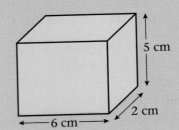

5 cm

2 cm

6 cm

3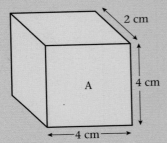

2 cm

4 cm

A

4 cm

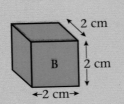

2 cm

B

2 cm

2 cm

a) Find the volume of cuboid A (Answer in cm³)

b) Find the volume of cube B (Answer in cm³)

c) How many B cubes are needed to make cuboid A?

4 Each week Jim gets £1 pocket money and his older brother, Alan, gets £3 pocket money.

Copy and complete the statement below to show the ratio of Jim's pocket money to Alan's pocket money.

Jim's money: Alan's money = ... : ....

5 For every £2 pocket money that Kylie gets, her older sister, June, gets £5.

a) If Kylie gets £8, how much money will June get?

b) If June gets £10, how much money will Kylie get?

6 Louis and Courtney share a bag of 32 sweets in the ratio 3:5.

How many sweets does each person get?

7 If 5 pencils cost 85p, find the cost of 8 pencils.

8 Here are the ingredients for 1 Victoria Sandwich Cake.

175 g   butter
175 g   caster sugar
3   eggs
175 g   self-raising flour
30 ml   jam

a) How many grams of caster sugar do you need to make *6* Victoria Sandwich cakes?

b) Write your answer to part (a) in kilograms.

c) How many millilitres of jam do you need to make *8* Victoria Sandwich cakes?

d) Write your answer to part (c) in litres.

9 Here is a *rough sketch* of a sector of a circle.

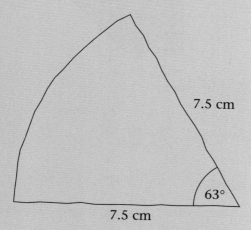

7.5 cm

7.5 cm

63°

Not to scale.

Use a *ruler, protractor and compasses* to make an *accurate, full size* drawing of this sector.

10 Use a *ruler* and *protractor* to make an *accurate* drawing of this triangle.

Measure the length of the side marked *x*.

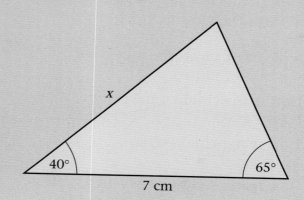

x

40°

65°

7 cm

11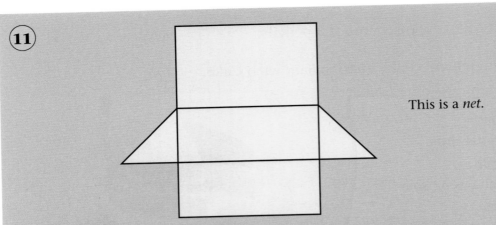

This is a *net*.

Which 3-D shape below could I make with my net?

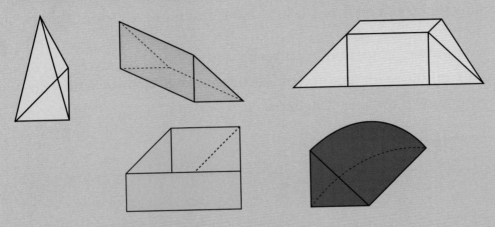

12 The shoe sizes of 15 people are listed below:

3 4 7 3 7 5 4 7
4 6 8 7 3 5 7

a) Which shoe size is the *mode*?

b) Write down the *range* of shoe sizes.

13 Terry has a part-time job. During 5 weeks he earns £23, £28, £23, £20 and £16. Find the mean average money for each week.

14 Daniel earns £12 each week for 20 weeks.
Shamina earns £11 each week for 22 weeks.
Who earns the most money?

15 This pie chart shows the eye colour of 36 children.

a) How many children have brown eyes?

b) How many children have green eyes?

c) How many children have grey eyes?

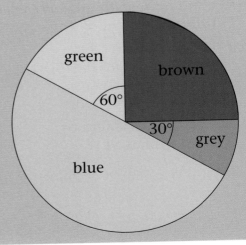

16 This stem and leaf diagram
shows the Science test scores
of 15 pupils.

The median is the middle number.

Write down the median Science test score.

4	2 2 5
5	1 3 3 7 8
6	2 3
7	4 4 6 9
8	2

17 The bar chart below shows what percentage of the world population speak each
language.

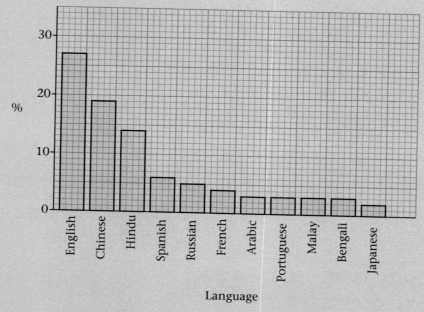

a) What percentage of the world population speak Chinese?

b) What percentage speak Russian?

c) What is the *difference* in the percentage of people who speak English
compared to French?

18 Write down the letter at each of
the following coordinates to
make a word.

(−4, −1)   (2, 1)   (2, −3)   (−2, 1)

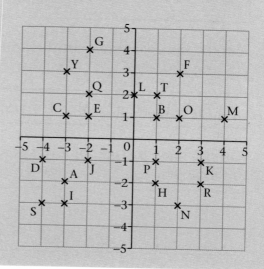

1 Draw a grid on squared paper like this.
Label across from 0 to 12 (horizontal axis).
Label up from 0 to 22 (vertical axis).

Plot the points below and join them up
with a ruler in the order given.

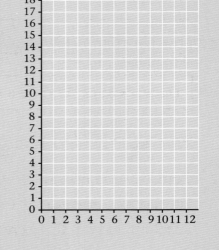

$(11, 4\frac{1}{2})$ $(11, 17)$ $(10, 21)$ $(4, 21)$ $(2, 17)$
$(2, 14)$ $(1\frac{1}{2}, 13)$ $(1\frac{1}{2}, 11\frac{1}{2})$ $(2, 11)$

On the same picture, plot the points below and
join them up with a ruler in the order given.

Do not join the last point in the box above with
the first point in the new box.

$(5, 21)$ $(6, 22)$ $(8, 21)$ $(8, 20)$

On the same picture, plot the points below and join them up with a ruler in the
order given.

$(6, 21)$ $(7, 22)$ $(8, 22)$ $(9, 21)$ $(9, 20)$

On the same picture, plot the points below and join them up with a ruler in the
order given.

$(2\frac{1}{2}, 3)$ $(5, 3)$ $(6\frac{1}{2}, 5)$ $(6\frac{1}{2}, 9)$ $(4, 10)$ $(2, 10)$ $(1, 8)$
$(4, 8)$ $(5, 7)$ $(5\frac{1}{2}, 6)$ $(5\frac{1}{2}, 5)$ $(5, 4)$ $(3, 4)$ $(3, 3)$

On the same picture, plot the points below and join them up with a ruler in the
order given.

$(3, 1\frac{1}{2})$ $(1\frac{1}{2}, \frac{1}{2})$ $(2\frac{1}{2}, 3)$ $(4, \frac{1}{2})$ $(5, 2\frac{1}{2})$ $(7, \frac{1}{2})$ $(11\frac{1}{2}, 2\frac{1}{2})$ $(11\frac{1}{2}, 4\frac{1}{2})$ $(5, 2\frac{1}{2})$

On the same picture, plot the points below and join them up with a ruler in the
order given.

$(2, 14)$ $(3, 14)$ $(4, 13)$ $(4, 12)$ $(4, 13)$ $(5, 14)$ $(7, 14)$ $(8, 13)$
$(8, 11)$ $(7, 10)$ $(5, 10)$ $(4, 11)$ $(4, 12)$ $(1\frac{1}{2}, 10\frac{1}{2})$ $(1\frac{1}{2}, 10)$ $(2, 10)$

On the same picture, plot the points below and join them up with a ruler in the order given.

(10, 11)   (11½, 11)   (11½, 12)   (10, 12)   (10, 14)   (11, 12)   (11½, 14)   (12, 12)

On the same picture, plot the points below and join them up with a ruler in the order given.

(2, 8)   (3½, 5)   (3½, 4)   (5, 5)   (5½, 5)   (5, 5)   (4½, 4)

Draw a • at (2, 12) and a • at (6, 12)

Who am I? Colour me in.

(2) Copy the grid below.

Label across from –6 to 10 (horizontal axis).

Label up from –6 to 10 (vertical axis).

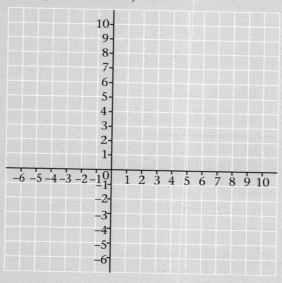

Plot the points below and join them up with a ruler in the order given.

(2, 0)   (2½, 1)   (5½, 1)   (6, 0)   (6, –2)   (5½, –3)   (2½, –3)   (2, –2)   (2, 0)

On the same picture plot the points below and join them up with a ruler in the order given.

Do not join the last point in the box above with the first point in the new box.

(3, 1)   (3, 2)   (1, 2)   (0, 3)   (0, 4)   (1, 5)   (3, 5)   (4, 4)   (5, 5)   (6, 5)
(7, 4)   (7, 3)   (6, 2)   (5, 2)   (5, 1)   (5, 2)   (4, 3)   (4, 4)   (4, 3)   (3, 2)

On the same picture, plot the points below and join them up with a ruler in the order given.

$(3, 7)$ $(3, 8)$ $(4, 8)$ $(5\frac{1}{2}, 8\frac{1}{2})$ $(5\frac{1}{2}, 6\frac{1}{2})$ $(4, 7)$ $(4, 8)$

On the same picture, plot the points below and join them up with a ruler in the order given.

$(5\frac{1}{2}, 0)$ $(5\frac{1}{2}, -2)$ $(3\frac{1}{2}, -2)$ $(3\frac{1}{2}, -1\frac{1}{2})$ $(5, -1\frac{1}{2})$ $(5, -\frac{1}{2})$ $(3\frac{1}{2}, -\frac{1}{2})$ $(3\frac{1}{2}, 0)$ $(5\frac{1}{2}, 0)$

On the same picture, plot the points below and join them up with a ruler in the order given.

$(4, 7)$ $(3, 7)$ $(1\frac{1}{2}, 6\frac{1}{2})$ $(1\frac{1}{2}, 8\frac{1}{2})$ $(3, 8)$

On the same picture, plot the points below and join them up with a ruler in the order given.

$(6, -1)$ $(8, -1)$ $(7, 2)$ $(10, 5)$ $(7, 6)$ $(6, 10)$ $(3, 8)$

$(1, 10)$ $(-1, 7)$ $(-4, 7)$ $(-3, 4)$ $(-5, 2)$ $(-3, 1)$ $(-3, -2)$

$(-1, -1)$ $(0, -4)$ $(4\frac{1}{2}, -4)$ $(5, -3)$

On the same picture, plot the points below and join them up with a ruler in the order given.

$(-2, 2)$ $(-3, 2)$ $(-3, 3)$ $(-2, 3)$

On the same picture, plot the points below and join them up with a ruler in the order given.

$(-2, 2\frac{1}{2})$ $(-2\frac{1}{2}, 2\frac{1}{2})$

Draw a • at $(1, 3)$ and a • at $(6, 3)$

Who am I? Colour me in.